*(Concluded from front flap)*

lishment of the Weston Electrical Instrument Company and his much-enjoyed legal entanglements. Today's electrical engineers will find it stimulating, and all who enjoy the accounts of colorful lives and personalities will find this story of Edward Weston absorbing and inspiring reading.

## About the author . . .

David O. Woodbury is ideally qualified for the writing of this book. A graduate engineer from the Massachusetts Institute of Technology, he has practiced as an electrical and research engineer and is a former news editor of *Power* magazine. He has been actively engaged as a free-lance interpreter of science since 1929, covering the technical fields for publishers, national magazines, and newspapers, including *Readers Digest, Saturday Evening Post, Science Digest,* and *Scientific American.*

Mr. Woodbury is author of many books on the various phases of science, and is well known for his radio work, lecturing, teaching, and consulting work. His vivid account of the life and times of Edward Weston attests to his unique ability to portray in realistic fashion historic happenings and famous people in science.

# A MEASURE FOR GREATNESS

BOOKS BY DAVID O. WOODBURY

*Communication*

*The Glass Giant of Palomar*

*The Colorado Conquest*

*What You Should Know about Submarine Warfare*

*Beloved Scientist*

*Builders for Battle*

*Battlefronts of Industry*

*A Measure for Greatness*

Edward Weston in the prime of life.

# A Measure for Greatness

A SHORT BIOGRAPHY OF

*EDWARD WESTON*

*by*

DAVID O. WOODBURY, A.B., B.S., M.S.

McGRAW-HILL BOOK COMPANY, INC.

*New York, Toronto, London*

*1949*

A MEASURE FOR GREATNESS

# Foreword

Biographies reciting the struggles in the lives and works of foundation electrical engineers who are gone are of great encouragement to the active exercise of originality, vision, and invention by young electrical engineers of the present generation. We are fortunate that publishers are now giving attention to the biographies and autobiographies of such older men, among whom Edward Weston was one. There is vastly more original work still to do in electrical engineering than was imagined in the days of Weston and his compeers, but it is encouraging that there is now infinitely more knowledge of the way to attack the problems that are now in our hands.

The miracles produced by electrical engineering came fundamentally to the light during the first quarter of the nineteenth century through the experimental researches of that extraordinary experimental scientist, Michael Faraday. He was stimulated to study electromagnetic relations from the discovery in 1820 made by the Danish scientist Hans Christian Oersted that the electric current affects a magnetic needle, and also by certain experiments with the electric current carried out by Sir Humphry Davy and other experimenters who left great names for disclosing our early understanding of electric currents.

From that early part of the nineteenth century onward a continuous stream of lesser discoveries have come into knowledge; but it was the last quarter of the nineteenth century before the broad applications for American electrical engineering of today were laid by the great inventors of that day—T. A. Edison, Charles Brush, Edward Weston, Elihu Thomson, Alexander Graham Bell, F. J. Sprague, and a galaxy of lesser men. These were followed by such as George Westinghouse, Sir William Thomson (Lord Kelvin), Oliver Heaviside, and lesser but still distinguished men, who entered the world field at a later date. The entire science and art of electronics are still more recent.

Weston, born in England in 1850, came to this country in his early manhood. He promptly went into business relating to electroplating apparatus and later expanded the business into developing electric lighting machinery and apparatus, in which he became one of our few very notable experimental designers and inventors in the early electrical engineering days. His was a determined type of mind, and with this quality he joined distinguished powers of origination. In the end, he ran through a career of designing and building dynamos for electric lighting service which were fine examples of good design and manufacture before the laws of the magnetic circuit became known.

Mr. Weston worked out for himself empirical plans for his designs of dynamos before the notable empirical formula for the magnetic circuit had been published by Gisbert Kapp and before Dr. John Hopkinson published the experimental laws of the magnetic circuit which put dynamo design on a rational foundation. When one looks at those Weston dynamos of the early 1880's and admires their attractive form and their efficiency, one half believes that Weston had in his mind in those early days the truly rational ideas of the then unknown laws.

Mr. Weston was a born mechanician of high order, which apparently aided him in the machinery design; and it was this, associated with his powers of origination, that led him into devising and manufacturing accurate portable electrical measuring instruments along lines that able men of experience then classed as impracticable; but his instruments promptly took a high place in appreciation in electrical engineering, which place they still hold. Along with these instruments, the need of low-temperature-coefficient shunts for the instruments led him to the invention of alloy metals of very low temperature coefficients or of even a negative coefficient. His early reports of this accomplishment were not generally accepted, but he took the opportunity of a gathering of electrical engineers and physicists from this country and abroad in 1893, which occurred in Chicago, to prove the accuracy of his reports.

In connection with his electrical measuring instruments, he also produced a standard electrical battery cell to be used in standardizing measurements of voltage that has taken the place of the formerly used famous Clark cell. This Weston cell is still used as an important standard in electrical engineering and physics.

Various other contributions to electrical engineering by Weston I can not here take space to enumerate, but those interested in the career of this great inventor will find them outlined in Mr. Woodbury's fine biography. In addition to his other great achievements, he may properly be called the father of accurate electrical measurements by portable instruments. These measurement achievements of themselves have been a fundamental contribution to the advancement of electrical engineering practice.

I first met Mr. Weston in the decade of the '80's while I was a graduate student of electrical engineering at Cornell University under the guidance of Professor William A. Anthony, for whom Weston had great admiration and whom he visited. I was deeply fascinated by Weston's talk of what he was doing in improving electric lighting and particularly what he was doing in the development of accurate electrical measuring instruments. He was a man of introvert qualities and did not cultivate many intimate friends, but my intimacy as a graduate student with Professor Anthony brought these early contacts thus referred to. For many years thereafter I came again in contact from time to time with Weston and always left him with a lively appreciation of his originality and brilliancy in pushing forward his work of invention. His name belongs with the group of the few great men who led the galaxy of distinguished electrical engineers of the United States and Europe and who laid by their inventions the foundations of what is now our great and useful structure of electrical engineering and the electrical engineering industries. His biography will provide an inspiring stimulant to the thinking of today's electrical engineers.

DUGALD C. JACKSON

Cambridge, Mass.
*August,* 1949

Inventors of that day often spent a lifetime on Item One; frequently they got no further.

A man with a mechanical idea was strictly on his own. He had to build his own tools, manufacture his own materials, devise his own means of making measurements and tests. The crudity of these things raised grave obstacles, often so buried the original idea in trivial difficulties that it was not workable at all. Thus, the early attempts to construct electrical machinery were severely hampered by the lack of insulated copper wire. Joseph Henry insulated his own, as he needed it, by winding it by hand with cotton thread. It was impossible to get wire of uniform cross section, for die drawing was still a crude art. And the variations in diameter prevented the design of apparatus that would carry into effect principles believed to be sound. Years of discouraging effort were often spent circumventing practical difficulties that actually had little to do with the main principles.

The discovery and development of the electric motor and dynamo is a case in point. When Faraday first discovered, in 1821, that a wire suspended beside the pole of a magnet would rotate around it when carrying current, he released a force so small that it seemed no more than an interesting demonstration. Ampère, in a similar experiment, did little better. It remained for Joseph Henry to show that real forces could be developed by large masses of iron wound with many turns of wire and powered by huge batteries. Henry produced an electric motor something like a modern seesaw. It consisted of a bar that teetered back and forth between two electromagnets, switching the current from one to the other continually. This motion could be translated into rotation by a crank. The device had little power. But a very important principle emerged directly, at the hands of Hyppolyte Pixii in Paris. Realizing that continual reversals were needed to cause steady rotation or reciprocation he invented the "commutator"—a metal cylinder composed of two insulated halves, rotating with the shaft of the "motor." Metallic brushes rubbed on this device, reversing the current flow with each half revolution. A year later, in 1833, William Ritchie in London produced strong rotation of a bar carrying two electromagnets past the two poles of a horseshoe magnet, using Pixii's commutator. The principle of the "electromechanical engine" was established.

But it was the wrong principle. The mutual pull of two magnets of opposite pole was a subsidiary phenomenon that was obvious, and easy to apply, but led to a dead end. The real fundamental—Faraday's wire rotating in a magnetic field—was too obscure to invite application for more than thirty-five years. Meanwhile, ingenuity and persistence on both sides of the ocean produced reciprocating electric motors that actually had power. To the Vermont blacksmith, Thomas Davenport, went the credit for the first industrially useful machine, when he constructed a motor weighing fifty pounds, which actually drove a drill press in his shop. This was in 1837. Two years later Jacobi, in Russia, propelled a boat by similar means. And the next year the Scotchman, Robert Davidson, built a motor that operated lathes, a carriage, and finally a railway train at the speed of four miles an hour.

Professor Charles G. Page, in this country, worked for thirteen years on a similar electromagnetic motor, which he called a "galvanic multiplier." Finally, in 1850, he persuaded Congress to appropriate $20,000 for further experiments and built a machine that delivered 1 horsepower. Much encouraged, Page went on immediately to construct larger models and eventually was rewarded by seeing a giant electric locomotive weighing twelve tons actually attain a speed of nineteen miles an hour on the Baltimore & Ohio Railroad. But by this time the government money was exhausted and Page had to abandon his experiments. It had become obvious to him, as to everyone else, that the inefficient push-pull of heavy electromagnets would never make an economical prime mover. Worse, the giant batteries of wet cells set an insurmountable limitation. They were expensive to build and were very soon exhausted by the heavy current drain. Once down, new metallic plates and new acid had to be put in. There appeared to be no commercial future for electric power along these lines.

The true principle of both dynamo and motor lay in full view in the Faraday copper-disk dynamo of 1831. This was simply a disk rotating between the poles of a magnet, current being picked up by brushes on the shaft and on the disk's rim. The success of the voltaic battery had completely obscured this basic discovery for many years. It was considered a laboratory toy. For twenty years after Faraday's discovery there were no more than a handful of attempts made to generate electric currents by mechanical rotation. Pixii was responsible for the first, as already noted. His main contribution was the "commutator," or direction changer, giving the current an intermittent but unidirectional character. It was an invention so basic that it has survived almost unchanged.

Ritchie, Saxton, and Clarke contributed similar electric dynamos in the decade of the 1830's, all using some form of commutator, and all constructed around the inefficient principle of moving bobbins of wire past the poles of a permanent magnet. Clarke's machine was the best, for he was an instrument maker in London and appreciated the value of good basic design. It was turned by hand and resembled the modern magneto. Presently it attained a firm place in the philosophical laboratories of the day and was used everywhere for class demonstrations. Clarke understood the basic relationship between the magnetic field and the number of turns of wire on the rotating armature, for he provided his dynamos with several such armatures, interchangeable in the bearings. An armature with a few turns of heavy wire produced a low voltage and considerable current; one with a great many turns of fine wire produced little current but a respectably high voltage.

Faraday, with true scientific genius, had immediately gone on from his first copper-disk dynamo to investigate the nature of magnetic forces and had named and defined the shape and strength of the "fields" around a magnet's poles. He had also discovered the laws of "induction," which stated that the voltage created in a wire passing through such a field depended upon the number of lines of force "cut" in a given time. Joseph Henry, working independently three thousand miles away, mounted two coils on an iron core and demonstrated the same principle in another form. When he started and stopped a current in one coil he detected a momentary "kick" or voltage in the other coil. This was the result of the motion of the lines of force through the turns of wire in the coil. Out of the second discovery came the modern induction coil and the transformer.

Thus, the two scientists had shown that it did not matter whether the turns of wire physically moved through a steady magnetic field, as Faraday arranged it, or whether the wire remained stationary and the field itself altered around the wire, as Henry had it. The two cases were identical in effect: magnetic "flux" cutting an electric conductor, produced a voltage in it; by completing the wire circuit, a current was generated that lasted as long as the field kept on changing. Both men proved that the voltage in the wire depended upon the length of wire (or the number of coil turns) and the strength of the field.

Here, in this simple fundamental, lay the secret of all magneto-electric apparatus. But simplicity is rarely obvious. It was two decades later that Hyjorth, in 1855, obtained the first patent on an electromagnetic machine. Two years later Werner Siemens in Germany invented a dynamo with a "shuttle" armature; that is, a moving element shaped like a cylinder, with a deep channel cut in each side to hold the turns of wire. A shaft passed through it lengthwise. This armature revolved *between the poles* of a permanent horseshoe magnet and hence caused the wire to cut across the magnetic field where the lines of force were strongest. In addition, the magnet poles were hollowed out to receive the armature with very little clearance, so that the flux flowed in a path broken only by the narrow gap. This last feature greatly increased the number of lines of force available to be cut. By placing several magnets side by side, the width of the field could be multiplied several times and the armature made quite long. This further increased the amount of wire actively generating voltage. For the first time, now, the dynamo was given a reasonable efficiency. The currents generated in the armature represented a fair percentage of the mechanical forces required to rotate the machine. Competition with the voltaic battery was possible.

There was still a long way to go, of course, for the proportions were not right, the armature wires were too small and the steel and cast iron of the magnetic circuit were poor flux conductors. It required twenty years more to master these details and to understand the theory of operation. But it was a significant start.

Siemens' first generator did not have a commutator; currents were taken from it by means of two insulated metal rings on the shaft, and hence changed direction of flow twice with every revolution of the armature. This was the world's first alternator. But there was no use for alternating currents, beyond the laboratory, and there only for stunts like the shocks that small Edward Weston had received. Such electricity was believed to neutralize itself and to give no net effect. Direct current was considered essential if this new force was to become commercially useful. Hence Siemens' later dynamos included commutators and were direct-current machines.

During the decade of the sixties inventors began to take the dynamo seriously. The electric arc light was coming. Electroplating of metals was already in common use. There were hints that mill machinery might some day be driven by electric motors. All of these applications depended upon an efficient dynamo.

Antonio Pacinotti opened the decade with several important advances in dynamo design. In the Siemens machine the armature coils were bunched, hence the wires actually cut magnetic lines of force less than half the time; during the rest of each revolution they were traveling more or less parallel to these lines and so did not generate a voltage. Pacinotti suggested a different arrangement: a ring armature with many coils distributed around it so that some part of the winding was crossing the field all the time. To this he added a great improvement: the commutator with many small separate segments, rather than only two. The coils were all joined together, and each junction terminated at a commutator segment. The result was that, as the armature revolved through the magnetic field, some of the coils were always cutting maximum flux. The brushes, rapidly connecting opposite pairs of commutator bars, thus were able to draw a large number of current pulses out of the machine and so produce a nearly steady current.

Pacinotti also found that a generator could be used equally well as a motor, without any alterations whatever. The art was on the right road at last.

Only one more element was needed to open the age of electric power—the elimination of permanent magnets on dynamo machines. This was first suggested by Henry Wilde, of Manchester, England, in 1866, when he tried using electromagnets to produce the stationary field of his machine. He made the discovery that a small permanent-magnet generator could be used to "excite" the field coils of a very much larger main dynamo, thus producing much larger currents than the small machine could do of itself.

Professor Farmer in America took the next step, by building a dynamo that was *self*-exciting, supplying from its own armature the small current needed to create its magnetic field. That same year, the Varleys of Atlantic cable fame patented a machine that had two separate field windings. These could be connected either in series or parallel, and placed across the armature circuit. Sir Charles Wheatstone, in the following year, described the action of these windings before the Royal Society, and himself took out patents on various circuit arrangements. Today, direct-current machines are universally provided with two field windings, a heavy one for connection in series with the armature, and a light one for connection in parallel. This "compounding" permits the machine to hold its voltage constant at all electrical loads. But though the English scientists are generally given credit for the invention, they did not then understand the principle, and no efficient design was produced. It remained for men like Gramme and Weston, half a dozen years later, to disclose the first effective arrangement of the coils.

5

In those days it was entirely logical for a boy of spirit and innate curiosity to concern himself with science rather than with games and enjoyments that had no constructive purpose beyond physical development. It was, perhaps, the only period in human history when youth could contribute to technical advance; before that there had been no such advance; later, the whole matter was to become so involved that years of careful training would be necessary before a young man could even master the terms in which progress was made. At any rate, Edward Weston in his early teens plunged straight into the business of chemistry and electricity, as professionally as if he had been a seasoned experimentalist. Though electricity was his chief interest, chemistry was his first love, because the chemical battery was the only generator of current that could be made at home by a boy.

The young investigator started off in a friendly and exciting environment—Wolverhampton. The city lay in the highly industrialized heart of British industry, a few miles from the great manufacturing center of Birmingham, and a hundred odd miles from London. Steel, textiles, and railroads were the main interests of the region, which was known as the "Black Country" because of the smoke and the grime. It was the temper of the people to work long hours and to accomplish much. Weston's father, it is probable, held the position of "mechanical engineer" in one of the mills, though there is no record of it. Nor is there a detailed record of Edward's early scientific exploits.

Weston was given the best education available, first in the grade schools of the town, then at St. Peter's Collegiate Institute in Wolverhampton. In those days scientific instruction, for those who had an aptitude for it, was much more personal; every student was given close attention by a recognized authority. At St. Peter's, Weston had the good fortune to receive private tutoring in chemistry and physics from a Fellow of the London Chemical Society, Henry A. Horton. Later, he continued his studies with William H. Harrison and Thomas Sherlock, also members of the Society. Each of them recognized the boy's talent for experimental work and gave him every opportunity to orient himself in the laboratory.

Edward soon decided to follow science as a life work. In this, he had the inspiration of several of the world's great scientists. Faraday, for one, was still lecturing at the Royal Society in London. An old man now, his wonderful personality was known and loved throughout England. It was one of Edward's ambitions to go to London as soon as he grew up and apprentice himself to Faraday. Unfortunately the great man died before he could do this. Another inspiration was Clerk Maxwell; still another, Lord Kelvin. The successful Atlantic cable was just then being laid under Kelvin's direction. In Germany, von Helmholtz was in the midst of his researches on light; in France, Pasteur was developing the germ theory of disease; in Germany again, Mendel was teaching his new principle of heredity. Edison was hard at work on the telegraph in America.

But Faraday interested Weston most. Much of his school time was spent in repeating Faraday's experiments with electricity and magnetism, descriptions of which he found in books obtained at the library.

Weston's mechanical aptitude amounted to more than a mere love for moving machinery. His hands were naturally skilled; he was not satisfied with simply observing how things worked, but taught himself the underlying principles by building models of everything that caught his eye. At the age of nine he was reading everything he could get in the way of technical books, and building with his own hands everything he could find materials for. Steam engines, of course, fascinated him, and he built models that worked, after a fashion. Induction coils, electric bells, motors, batteries, telegraphs, electric clocks—all followed in due course.

To do all this the boy needed more space than his classrooms could spare him. So he set up a laboratory in one of the rooms in his father's house and filled it with every conceivable apparatus and chemical. It was much to the credit of his family, and no doubt due mostly to his mother's fine spirit, that the dirt and noise, and especially the imminent danger of explosion, were borne without protest. Edward's personality, even at this early stage, was strong enough to give his boyhood experimental work validity. If he said he intended to experiment with hazardous machines, nobody was likely to deny him the privilege.

Electricity interested Edward more than any other new thing; so, naturally, he determined to build an electric motor. This was no easy task, especially since the motors of the day were pretty crude affairs. Not hoping to generate any real power, but only to make a machine that would turn round, Weston adopted the original model invented by Joseph Henry—a single electromagnet alternately pulling and releasing a bar connected to a crankshaft and flywheel. The device itself was simple enough. But an appreciation of the forces involved, and especially of the function of the commutator cam in making and breaking the circuit at the right moment, was unusual indeed in a boy of twelve. He had no "how to build it" books to follow.

Long afterward, the inventor described his trials in overcoming his first real design problems on this little electric motor, sketching the apparatus for the editor of an electrical magazine as he talked. "My greatest trouble," he remembered, "was in obtaining suitable insulated wire (for winding the magnet). Although the town in which I lived was one of 150,000 inhabitants, there was not one electrical supply store in the place"—which was natural enough. There was no electrical industry to require it. "Of course, bare copper wire was easily obtainable, but wire with insulation on it was another thing." So the boy had to insulate his own wire, just as Henry himself had done thirty years before. The machine he built for the job demonstrated that he had a true sense of mechanical arrangement, and a wealth of inventive ability. Like Faraday, he had a scientific mind, searching out the heart of a problem rather than "gadgeting" his way around it.

Mr. Weston continued his reminiscenses: "It would appear at first sight, to anyone not familiar with such winding machines, that with this little device I could have done fairly good work with but little trouble. You have no idea, though, how expert I had to become in the manipulation of the two handles to produce wire that was really insulated. Unless I moved both handles at certain fixed speeds I left gaps between the convolutions of the cotton. I overcame this difficulty by the use of brown cotton on one spool and white on the other. Thus, the instant my windings became irregular I detected the change and could adjust the speed to suit."

The ability to make considerable lengths of insulated wire stimulated the boy's interest in other electrical apparatus. He now tried winding an induction coil—what was then known as a Ruhmkorff coil—for making sparks. From this he went on to the more practical instrument, the telegraph. The small line that he built, with its tickers and keys, worked perfectly. The overhead wires were insulated from their wooden supports by the necks of bottles—a scheme used by many generations of boys that have come after.

Edward's experimental work was solidly backed by constant reading, and in Smee's *Elements of Electro-Metallurgy* he found an application of electricity which fascinated him and which later became the basis for his start in the commercial world. Electroplating was an art already well understood, but young Weston was more interested in the fundamentals of electrochemistry than in plating bits of metal. Besides, silver, the most common plating material, was far too expensive for him. At the time, his most urgent need was for a source of electric current of sizable proportions, and so he determined to build himself a chemical battery, after the latest designs then in use. The Grove cell was the one most commonly employed in telegraphy, but Weston was unable to build one because the central electrode had to be made of platinum, which he could not afford to buy. He therefore adopted the Bunsen design, which was cheaper but somewhat more difficult to make.

Bunsen's battery, invented in 1842, consisted of a jar of dilute sulphuric acid containing a hollow cylinder of zinc for the negative electrode and a rod of carbon for the positive. A dense, homogeneous grade of carbon was necessary to withstand the action of the acid. No such carbon could be bought in Wolverhampton. But young Weston solved the problem in a unique way: by obtaining it for nothing from the local gas works.

Ever since childhood he had been a constant visitor to the factories surrounding the town. The owners of these plants, then among the largest in the world, were friends of his father, and Edward had no trouble in being admitted to the dark and smoke-filled buildings where the clank of steam hammers and the brilliant blasts of the Bessemer converters dominated every other sound and sight. The boy's love for machinery held him in these places for hours on end, and his natural curiosity drove him to investigate every piece of apparatus and every process till he knew them all intimately, in principle and practice. There was no more entrancing display than in the gas works, where he saw the huge coking ovens roasting the coal to drive off the volatile hydrocarbons. Edward learned the chemistry of the whole process and knew many of the foremen and workmen by their first names. They let him climb up and down over the machinery to his heart's content.

Edward Weston knew that the gas coke was carbon, more or less pure. But it was mostly very porous and crumbled easily. It occurred to him that there should be more dense samples of it deposited on the inner surfaces of the "stills" in which the coking was done. Waiting until one of these was taken out of service for cleaning, he got permission to climb inside, and there he found exactly what he was looking for—lumps of dense, fine-grained carbon clinging to the roof of the still at the end where the fire was hottest. Filling his pockets with chunks of this he ran home to see what he could do.

It was a discovery that gave young Weston the battery carbon he needed. But it was much more. Twenty years later, at the height of the competition to invent better incandescent lamp filaments in America, Weston was able to produce and patent one of the most serviceable carbon threads ever discovered, using a process of hardening based on his observations at the coking ovens. This was a fine example of the kind of mind that was to bring forth the new electrical age: a mind capable of recording basic principles from wide observation, then integrating and applying them to new problems.

### 6

In the course of his youthful experiments Weston accumulated a good deal of apparatus and an extraordinary knowledge of natural science and engineering. Being a boy of strong personality he was soon taking a leading part in his class and was highly regarded by his teachers. This led, at the age of sixteen, to his first public appearance, presumably before a group of interested laymen who, as was the habit of the times, kept abreast of the mechanical arts by going to a course of lectures. There is no record of this first public talk, but young Weston probably showed his battery and used it to demonstrate the action of motors, bells, induction coils, and other apparatus, all made by himself. His success must have been considerable, for he was asked to lecture again, and did so, at about the same period.

But his interest was not so much in telling of his discoveries as in making more. His school years were finished, therefore, in the enviable job of assisting his professors in making demonstrations to their classes. On one memorable day, the boy helped connect up a large battery of cells to run one of the earliest electric lamps. It was still ten years before the incandescent lamp would be made practical by Edison. And in one other field he contributed a valuable thought, though it came to no practical end then. This was when he suggested the use of rubber tires for a "steam carriage" that was proposed for use on the highways. He believed that they would prevent the hard rims of the wheels from cutting the road surface. But Weston had no funds or opportunity for making experiments in this field; the suggestion lay dormant till rubber tires became the fashion on horse-drawn vehicles much later in the century.

When Edward Weston's school career ended, the question came up as to what profession he should follow. In our own day he would no doubt have gone to some technical institute, to prepare for an engineering or scientific career. But in the mid-nineteenth century such opportunities were not open to young men without money, and the Weston family was not well off. Besides, it was customary for a boy's career to be chosen for him by his parents. So, with some misgivings, Edward submitted to apprenticeship to a dental surgeon named Owen, in Wolverhampton. His father felt that his mechanical bent ought to express itself well in this pursuit. It did not. The boy detested any other teeth than his own and refused to become interested. The engagement ended in a few weeks.

But the parents seemed determined that their son should be a physician of some sort. In their conservative judgment it was the only profession that a mechanically minded youth should follow. So arrangements were made for him to receive his formal medical training. This resulted in a valuable though painful three years in which Weston learned little medicine but got a fine grounding in chemistry.

It was the custom of the day for a medical student to apprentice himself to a doctor and assist him in his practice. Young Edward was lucky to be accepted by two brothers, Drs. E. H. and H. M. Coleman. The elder man, Dr. E. H. Coleman, was a distinguished and kind-hearted old gentleman who had a natural sympathy and understanding for youth. He liked Edward at once and took him to live in his own home, a thing which was frequently done at the time to give the training a more personal touch. Edward was so pleased with the change from the obnoxious dental surgery that he applied himself with great vigor and began to think that a medical career would not be bad. His work interested him immediately, for it had a practical touch. Besides his formal studies he was allowed to mix medicines in the drug closet and assist at various minor operations which the doctors were continually performing. The chemistry which was involved, interested him especially. His understanding of the subject was already so good and his eagerness to learn more so great that Dr. Coleman was delighted to take special pains with him and give him unusual responsibility.

Coleman was not only a good practicing physician but a scientist himself, and had collected quite a large assortment of philosophical apparatus. In the evenings and in off hours he took delight in setting up experiments with Edward, painstakingly guiding him in the intricacies of chemical and electrical theory. As time went on, the boy spent more and more of his hours in the laboratory and talked of it incessantly whenever he went home of a Sunday.

His parents were annoyed. The opportunity to study the profession of medicine under a fine teacher was a rare one. For Edward to divert even a little of his attention to such "tomfoolery" as playing with electricity was little less than a crime. It was a sure sign that he lacked application and did not appreciate his advantages. There were many bitter arguments at home over this, arguments in which Edward would at first defend himself vehemently, then become sullen and silent and march off to his room at the Colemans' to plunge himself still further into his beloved experiments.

It must be admitted that young Weston was not putting his whole mind on his medical work. As the months went by, the job of becoming a doctor irked him more and more. Mixing chemicals became a dull task and listening to the interminable complaints of patients was worse. Furthermore, he was apt to be routed out of bed at all times of night when there were emergencies to attend to. One bothersome task, which seemed to him rather a joke as he looked back on it years later, was to determine the solvency of a midnight caller before letting him in. There were of course no telephones then; some relative or friend of the sick man would arrive outside the house and raise the doctor by shouting or throwing pebbles at the window. It was Edward's duty to thrust his head out and ask the visitor what time it was. If he answered correctly, the doctor would dress and go with him to the patient. Coleman assumed that anyone who owned a clock could afford to pay his bill.

Things went from bad to worse with young Weston's medical career, and gradually a positive hatred of the profession gathered in his heart. In his second year of apprenticeship to Dr. Coleman, England was swept by a fearful epidemic of smallpox. A tenth of the population died. Sleepless nights and constant fear of the disease as he helped the fine old doctor in his blind fight against a scientific mystery, only served to increase his impatience with the whole profession. In the third year of his novitiate a cholera epidemic passed through the land, and the same thing happened, only worse.

But it was two relatively small incidents that clinched his decision to abandon medicine. One day toward the end of his course, Edward was deeply occupied in the laboratory with an electrical experiment when a gentleman came in to have a boil lanced. This sort of work Dr. Coleman left for Edward to do, but the foolish apprentice hurriedly told the patient he would have to wait, perhaps some little time, until the experiment was finished. The man fell into a great rage and stamped out, shouting that he would never come to the Colemans' again. Edward was told afterward that this sort of conduct could not be condoned in a doctor. Medicine, said his friend, might not be the right profession for him, after all.

The second incident climaxed and symbolized the boy's whole dislike of doctoring. With his diploma in hand, he was ready to go on visits to patients. One of his first was a case of typhoid fever, with rheumatic symptoms added. Weston confidently diagnosed the rheumatism and prescribed the right treatment for it. But he entirely missed the more serious malady. The patient became alarmingly ill and would have died if Edward had not hastily sum moned Dr. Coleman to help him. Together, they managed to pull the woman through. Weston does not seem to have blamed himself for the mistake so much as he blamed the practice of medicine itself. It served mainly to fix his determination to leave the profession. This he did within a few weeks.

But not without the bitter opposition of his parents and some of his friends. They felt that he was plainly foolhardy to abandon a promising career, and said so. Edward's answer was equally vehement:

"I wouldn't be a doctor under any circumstances. Surgery is all right, but there is nothing scientific about the practice of medicine. You guess what effect certain drugs will have but you can't determine accurately."

No doubt the family had a broader view of the physician and appreciated the human values of his skill as well as the purely scientific ones. But to their son the primary purpose of science was to be exact and predeterminable. That he understood and that he wanted to follow. The argument caused serious friction at home. To avoid further interference he decided to leave, going up to London to find work that he liked. He took with him a letter of introduction to Professor John Tyndall.

It was the winter of 1870. Professor Tyndall, for many years a celebrated physicist and authority on electricity and magnetism, was at that time superintendent of the Royal Institution in London. An intimate friend of Faraday, he had succeeded him in that position in 1867, upon the great scientist's death. Edward Weston worshiped Faraday. His greatest desire was to apprentice himself in the Institution, as Faraday himself had done fifty years earlier. Tyndall might well open the door to his ambition. If he was successful, the dismal years of medical study could soon be forgotten.

# PART TWO

# The Young Organizer

---

I

On the train from Wolverhampton to London, Edward Weston's future was suddenly cast in a completely different and unexpected mould. In the compartment he occupied there happened to be a voluble American tourist—one of those perennial, self-appointed salesmen of the New World who consider it their mission to invade foreign countries and spread glowing accounts of the homeland. The young Englishman, anxious to justify his own decision in leaving home, had soon told him of his aspirations in science and his belief in himself as a scientist. With this unusual opportunity before him, the American set out to make a convert in earnest. The chances for advancement in the United States, he said, were far and away superior to anything that England could offer. It would be folly for young Weston to lose himself in the musty confines of the Royal Institution when, for a mere trip acros the Atlantic, there would be unlimited scope to expand, many hundreds of choices of employment, and boundless horizons for success in the mechanical arts. "Why, now, you take New York City alone . . ."

Weston was convinced; he wondered why he had never thought of it himself. When he left the train he had a very different idea of the demands he would make upon prospective employers in London.

He soon found that his new friend had been right. For several weeks he tried to get a job and failed. There was no opening at the Institution, nor could he find employers looking for bright young scientists. Discouraged, and at the same time happy, he resolved to make the great experiment. Without waiting to consider the wisdom of it, he spent practically all the money he had for a steamship ticket to New York, then went home to pack up.

"My decision to come to the United States on a stranger's advice," he said afterward, "caused a great row with my family, but they could not persuade me to stay in England." They argued the great risk involved and the importance of family loyalty. They told him that they could not help him with a penny. But his mind was made up. At twenty, Edward Weston was already a hard-headed man who believed in his own abilities. He had no illusions about the difficulties of a scientific career. It was a practical profession in which a vast, unexplored territory lay open to the man who could accept the severe discipline and great risks of the pioneer. But it offered enormous opportunity just then—an opportunity to develop new applications which would benefit the whole world, bring fame to the successful, and perhaps provide a fortune, too. The only requirements, Weston decided, were a willingness to work very hard, a high degree of intellectual honesty, and unrelenting loyalty to high standards. Those requirements he could satisfy. Let the Land of Opportunity make him a rich man, if it would.

Edward had a pretty bad passage across the Atlantic on a small steamer whose name we do not know. He arrived in New York in May, 1870, groggy and thin. His entire wealth consisted of some books, one or two favorite pieces of homemade apparatus, a Bible, and a few pounds in cash. Beyond these, he had a pocket full of letters to scientific men of some distinction, mostly professors in eastern colleges. The prospects did not look very bright.

In those days there was no Ellis Island. Ships anchored in the harbor and were visited by customshouse officers, who went through the passengers' papers. Then the new arrivals were allowed to come ashore for their formal reception to the new land. This was done at the Battery, in the old Castle Garden, once famous as the opera house where Jenny Lind had sung. Even in 1870 the Battery still had an air of elegance. Many imposing old mansions were still standing, relics of a bygone day when well-dressed and prosperous-looking people had moved on the sidewalks. New York gave an air of prosperity and friendliness to its welcome.

The treatment accorded immigrants by the Government was re-

markably good. While they waited for their baggage at the Landing
Depot, they found good stores along the docks, where they could
purchase first necessities at reasonable prices. Nearby was a money
exchange office, where foreign currency was converted into American dollars. There was also a department somewhat like the modern
Travelers Aid Society, and here the strangers could find names and
addresses of boarding houses, eating places, and clothing stores that
were guaranteed not to overcharge. The proprietors of these places
were registered by the Government and were held strictly account-
able; any attempt at gouging the innocent visitors got them expelled
from the list. Most important was a labor exchange, where new
arrivals could get temporary jobs if they intended to stay in the city.

It was even possible to get free medical attention upon application, after being sent to Ward's Island Emigrant Refuge and
Hospital.

One piece of good advice given to everybody was a warning
against swindlers. The Government knew full well what advantage
was taken of helpless strangers, and intended to fortify them if it
could.

Weston accepted the offer of a boarding house address but
decided to go on his own for the rest. He was still much impressed
with the marvelous picture his American friend had painted for him.

Since he wished to be a chemist, he began by visiting every
chemical house he could locate. He did not want to present his
letters until he was sure that he couldn't find a job on his own. But
to his amazement he could find nobody who needed a young man
whose qualifications were mostly aspirations. Weeks went by and
presently he had tramped through every borough of New York
City and far out on Long Island as well, without success of any
kind. He was down now to abject poverty; many a day he could
allow himself no more than ten cents for all his meals. It looked
as if he would have to write home for help.

Rather than do this he began a systematic presentation of his
letters and met with the same result. Among others, he called upon
Professor Charles F. Chandler, who had just come to Columbia
College from Lehigh University to establish the Columbia School
of Mines. Dr. Chandler was a chemist himself, and just the under-

standing kind of man Weston had been looking for. But his friendly attitude did not yield a job. The new school was being started on a shoestring budget, and Chandler could afford to employ only experienced mining experts. The best he could do was to give the young man more letters to New York firms and send him once more on his weary rounds.

At the very last minute, however, Edward fell into a piece of luck and got a position as helper in the chemical manufacturing firm of William H. Murdock & Company on Broome Street. His career was under way at last.

All his life Weston remembered Chandler's kindness, and they were firm friends. There was a fairy-tale element in it, too. Forty-five years later, it was Dr. Chandler who presented him with the coveted Perkin medal for outstanding achievement in chemistry before a gathering of the most brilliant chemists in America.

2

Murdock's principal business was the manufacture of photographic chemicals. Those were the days when every photographer made his own "wet" plates at the scene of his picture taking. A syrupy solution of light-sensitive silver salts in collodion was actually flowed onto the glass in a dark room and the plate then loaded into the camera for exposure. The picture must be snapped at once, before the emulsion had had time to dry. The famous Civil-War photographer, Mathew Brady, had taken some remarkable battle pictures, hurrying around after the Union Army with a light-tight tent, in which he prepared his plates. This feat was greatly to his credit, for the collodion solutions were not uniform, emulsion speeds varied puckishly, and there was always the danger of explosion within the tent if the enemy did not demolish it from without.

Murdock's took what care they could in preparing the solutions, and Edward found that he could get invaluable training in practical chemistry in his job of mixing the ingredients. But it was a risky business, for the making of collodion was nothing other than the manufacture of guncotton. Nor was this being done under safe conditions. The "factory" was the basement of a four-story house in what was then the center of the New York business district. The chemicals were compounded in open trays ranged on benches around the place. There were no ventilating fans, no hoods for disposing of fumes, no fire protection at all. Murdock "ran for luck" with the silent blessing of the city government, which, under the lavish management of the Tweed Ring, had not found it important to worry about fire ordinances.

The inevitable explosion occurred a few weeks after Weston had taken the position. An expansive visitor came in one day, lit a cigar, and tossed the match—into a tray of guncotton. Fortunately, the tray was open to the air and did not blow up violently. Only one person was injured. With quick presence of mind Weston snatched up some sheets of wrapping paper lying nearby and smothered the flaming tray. He had long ago observed that it was difficult to ignite solidly folded paper.

He came out of the experience unscathed, physically. But he had had enough. His solid English common sense told him that it wasn't worth the risk to continue, literally playing with fire, with such crude equipment and no safeguards whatever. Moreover, the two proprietors of the place had escaped into the street the moment the blaze had started, leaving their employees to get on as best they could. Obviously, the management was inadequate. So he decided to quit.

It was not fear but his outraged sense of efficiency that decided him.

But quitting was not so easy. He had spent months finding this job; another would be still harder to locate. It is true that he was putting in a few extra hours a week as a part-time assistant to Dr. Charles F. Stone, Professor of Chemistry at Cooper Union. This job also had come his way through Dr. Chandler. But the position paid almost nothing and held no future. Caution bade him remain with Murdock until he should find something better. Luckily, this did not take so long as he feared.

Studying the want ads in the daily papers, he finally ran across something very promising. An advertiser needed a man with some electrical and chemical knowledge, particularly in electroplating work. Weston instantly jumped at the chance. He had been fascinated with electrochemistry since boyhood and had made many experiments with it. He sat down at once and wrote a letter applying for the position. It was characteristic of Edward that he crossed his bridges on the run, not even stopping to burn them. What lay behind him ceased to interest him. He took with him out of the past whatever of experience and facility he had gained and set his face forward without regret. A man who could do this in an age of swift change was pretty sure to make a success of himself. This young man did just that.

The day after Edward answered the ad a nattily dressed man came to Murdock's to see him. He proved to be William H. Belden, president of the American Nickel Plating Company on Howard Street. Belden instantly impressed the youthful chemist as a man of affairs, accustomed to ask only for expert opinion. It quickly turned out that this was what he wanted, and wanted badly. Although the American Company was one of the two largest plating concerns in New York, it was practically on the rocks. Its chemical solutions wouldn't plate; its business was rapidly disappearing.

"I am a stockbroker by profession," Belden told him, "and I know nothing of the technical side of the business. But neither do any of our employees. We are in such a bad way that I have even tried to operate the baths myself, naturally without success. What I must have is a man who understands these things scientifically, who can dig in immediately and rectify our troubles before it is too late."

"I understand electroplating very well," said Weston. "I believe I can find your trouble."

That was all Belden wanted to know. He hired the young man on the spot, at fifteen dollars a week, to fill the position of chemist and electrician for the firm. It would be up to him to set the company on its feet.

Weston's conscience, however, would not let him walk out of Murdock's without due notice. He told Belden that he would have to continue where he was for two weeks, till his present employer could get someone to fill his place.

Belden was irritated. "Do you mean that I shall have to wait two weeks before anything can be done? That will be suicide for us."

"No," said Weston, "I will work for you nights and Sundays, till I am through here."

The broker could not help admiring this fine spirit. The deal was closed immediately.

### 3

Weston showed up at the plating plant on Howard Street that night, with his jaw set and determination in his heart. He was an expert now, not merely hired help. It was a grand feeling to know that someone depended on him; it never occurred to him that his knowledge and experience might not be nearly enough to solve this serious problem. He took comfort in the fact that the electroplating art was still very crude. No one really understood the workings of it beyond the rule-of-thumb procedure that had grown out of twenty years of practical experience. This gave him the lead for a new approach—a purely chemical approach in which he would treat electroplating as a science to be built up by combining the principles of electricity and chemistry into a new and exact art. He would be more than an expert—a researcher and an inventor of new methods. He plunged into the job as if his life depended upon it, and in those two weeks put the plant back into shape. He did not sleep very much; a nap snatched now and then on a wooden bench when exhaustion overtook him was all that he permitted himself.

He soon discovered that there was no one thing the matter with the company's methods. Everything was wrong: the plating solutions were impure; the batteries, then universally used for furnishing current, were worn out; the objects to be plated were dirty; and the workmen were careless and inexpert. The condition of the electrolytes was the most flagrant source of trouble. A quick chemical analysis showed him that they were badly contaminated with copper from the cathode bars. The result was that newly plated objects would immediately begin to peel so that customers would send them back to be plated again. Weston's remedy was to throw some of the solutions away, "clean" others by precipitating out the copper. In his two weeks of night work the young scientist had put his worst difficulties behind him; the plant was in production again.

As soon as he had left Murdock for good, he settled down to

revamping the American Company's processes completely. Systematically he began a study of nickel plating from the ground up. With his characteristic thoroughness and love of detail he overhauled every item of the routine, questioning everything, searching for a better way to do each part of the process. He was teaching himself at the same time that he was acting as an expert, but he was careful not to say so.

In the five years that followed this chance answering of a newspaper ad, Edward Weston went far toward revolutionizing the art of electroplating. The improvements and simplifications that he made in every phase of the process were gradually adopted by others and have become the basis of the modern art of depositing metals. If he had been a little older and more experienced, he would have realized the commercial value of his improvements and would have patented them. As it was, the young man's enthusiasm for achievement was so great that he did not notice the commercial opportunities inherent in his ideas, and so passed up his first chance for a substantial income.

The first real crudity that Weston eliminated was the slipshod method of cleaning the work before plating it. The operators, he found, had no idea of the critical nature of the electrochemical reactions in the baths and hence took no measures to avoid contamination of the surfaces to which the nickel was supposed to adhere. Thus, to prepare objects for plating, they merely buffed them, then dipped them in a boiling solution of caustic potash to remove grease, and then scrubbed the potash off again with pumice and water and a brush.

The patents under which the company was doing its plating—granted to Dr. Isaac Adams and licensed to them by their rival, the United Nickel Plating Company—specifically stated that caustic potash would vitiate the electrolyte of the baths. Thus, extraordinary measures were taken to scour the potash off, and usually the work piece was badly scatched, especially when it was made of brass or copper. Weston immediately made careful studies of the solutions and found that reasonable traces of potash did no harm whatever. He then did away with the pumice treatment and substituted a thorough washing. The work improved at once.

Another phase of the precleaning problem, which bothered the plant a great deal and wasted days of time, was the "stripping" of old nickel plate from objects sent in to be refinished. One annoying job that came in about this time was typical: a large copper coffee urn that would not hold its plate and had been back three times for a new coat. On the third occasion a workman spent a whole week trying to remove the old plating from the curves and pockets of the brass. Weston was much disturbed by the inefficiency of such hit-or-miss methods and went to work to see what could be done about it. Shortly, he had invented an "acid dip" which stripped off old nickel plate in a few minutes and left the metal clean and unscratched underneath. The fourth time the urn was plated, it stayed plated.

Within a month of his first attack upon inefficiency the company began to prosper again. A thorough overhaul of the plating solutions had resulted in a better, more homogeneous coating of nickel which adhered tightly to the metal underneath and did not peel. Rejects and returned work dropped considerably. In addition, complicated shapes that could not be precleaned properly by mechanical methods, could now be securely plated even on their most inaccessible parts. Still more, Weston improved upon the methods of polishing the finished plate which gave a luster never before attained. He was altogether a valuable find for Belden.

But it was impossible for him to settle down to a dead level of production. Merely to keep the plating plant running did not interest him; it must be improved still further. So he decided to invent a malleable nickel plating. Electrodeposited nickel was extremely hard, difficult to polish, and likely to strip off under extremes of temperature in service. Weston envisioned a coating of soft metal which could be burnished like silver and would wear "forever." But he could not get it to come out that way except by reducing the current through the bath so greatly that very little hydrogen was formed. Hydrogen, he discovered, promoted hard, brittle nickel plate and increased the tendency for the bright metal to part company with the material underneath. But the price of avoiding it was a serious increase in plating time.

It was a question of compromise—something that he would be

forced to accept all his life with reluctance—and the compromise in this instance was to accept the hydrogen and the brittleness in return for a plating speed that would get the work out commercially fast.

In the course of his electrolysis studies, the young experimenter made an investigation of the plating quality as determined by the amount of current flowing through the cells. Like everything else in the art, the battery output had been standardized everywhere at two volts, delivered by parallel-connected pairs of Smee cells. This type of cell was used because its voltage held nearly constant under load. The current was determined by the strength of the solution and the amount of area being plated.

Weston soon decided that a constant voltage was undesirable. He found that in the early stages of depositing nickel on "inferior" metals such as brass and steel, a secondary reaction tended to occur with the nickel in solution, plating the work in spots with nickel *compounds* which adhered badly. The shop's method of overcoming this was to make the plating so thick that these rough spots were buried and would not tend to flake off. In working large objects with irregular contours and angles, it had always been necessary to scrape the bad spots clean by hand, then replate till they were covered. The serious loss of time and the waste of nickel were what Weston wanted to eliminate. His solution, which would be commonplace in research today, was brilliant and original then: He set up a special preliminary plating bath using a higher voltage, so that work placed in it received a thin film of pure nickel rapidly —too quickly for harmful side reactions to take place. Once covered, the object was then transferred to a standard bath and plated slowly, as usual. No bad spots could then appear. When this new system was installed, the savings in time and metal were immediate and impressive.

Weston's success with the American company soon gave him a position of authority in the whole electroplating field. It was not long before others came to consult him. Among them was a chemist who had started a small plating firm in Newark, N. J. After this had been running a short time the process began to give a black, powdery deposit and large amounts of hydrogen—and the inevitable high percentage of rejects. Weston went to Newark to see what was the matter. Obviously, he saw, it was a case of contamination.

"I cross-examined the workmen at the plant," he said afterward, "but no one would admit doing anything to the solution; yet I could not correct it. Then I questioned them even more closely and finally they admitted that the tank had leaked and that they had saved the plating solution by transferring it to a barrel—a 'clean' alcohol barrel!"

Weston could not imagine what there might have been in an alcohol barrel that would harm a plating solution, unless it was glue that had worked out of the seams. But the men insisted that it had been thoroughly scrubbed out. To make sure, he made a solution of potassium permanganate, which would react with gelatin, if any were present, and added it to the plating bath. The telltale pinkish tinge soon appeared. Turning on the current, he found that the plating proceeded normally, with no further trouble from hydrogen. This gave him one more item of fundamental knowledge of the art: even traces of organic matter will ruin plating baths. They must be chemically correct in every respect to do proper work.

## 4

During the year 1871 the American Nickel Plating Company thrived under Weston's energetic technical direction. Although William Belden took no direct part in running the company, he was extremely active in obtaining new business for it. Once the company began to do well, Belden showed a positive genius for discovering new objects that could be plated, and produced a long list of business and political friends who readily "fell" for his sales talk. The tremendous post-Civil War boom was still in progress, and, as in the fantastic period of the 1920's, people were ready to gamble heavily on any new thing that came along. Work piled up, and soon there was a waiting list. Every kind of material was offered for plating: cast iron, pewter, and many others. Weston was kept on the jump developing new wrinkles in chemistry to meet the new problems.

Everything imaginable seemed to look better under a plating of shiny nickel: metal buttons, belt buckles, keys, locks. Belden came in one day with a broad smile on his face. He had just persuaded the city fathers to nickel-plate New York's new fire engines. "Parts of them, that is," he added. "Even the huge bulbs used for equalizing pump pressure, and the tops of the boilers themselves." These were by all odds the largest objects ever plated; Weston had to use considerable ingenuity to accommodate the company's overworked equipment to this new demand. But Belden was still not satisfied. He now proposed that all the cast-iron lamp posts in town be nickel-plated, too. Fortunately, the politicians demurred and the mad idea was never carried out. It would have cost the taxpayers a fortune and made their city as ornate as a Hollywood stage set.

With all this Edward Weston, aged twenty-one, was doing pretty well. In just one year from his landing at Castle Garden he had become a recognized authority in a new and important industry. He had made valuable contributions to one of the most useful applications of electric power. And he was beginning to make money. Although the record does not say so, he had presumably got a raise from the American Nickel Plating Company. He might even be earning twenty-five dollars a week.

This being so, he decided to get married. It was a logical thing to do. He had spent a lonely first year in New York. America had given him a much chillier welcome than he had expected, but this was forgotten now in the stimulation of having conquered the new country so quickly. Never one to suffer from self-doubt, Edward was feeling his oats in good shape. He was a rising young inventor with a position to keep up. It was time to strike out for a social position in the community, establish a home, and be somebody.

Perhaps this was not exactly the pattern recommended to rising young geniuses who, in America, have always been expected by the bride's parents to offer a comfortable living and splendid prospects in return for the fair hand. But it was a much more realistic pattern. Weston needed a helpmate. Besides, the girl he had chosen had no parents to pass upon his qualifications. She and her brother were immigrants like himself. According to the custom in those days, they had come over with a group of young people, sent by their families to escape the dreary lack of opportunity in Europe. The parents frequently did not have the enterprise to come themselves. Thus the youthful pioneers were virtually orphans.

The young lady's name was Wilhelmina Seidel. She was flaxenhaired and buxom, a typical farm girl from the Central German village of Blankenheim. Her brother Ernest was a huge hulk of a man, not too brilliant and not overly ambitious. Wilhelmina's principal desire was to become a good housewife and mother and take care of an industrious but not necessarily brilliant husband. This was not exactly what she got, for she was destined to become the wife of a millionaire inventor and business organizer who would go down in history as a great scientific pioneer. She understood nothing of science or the scientific mind, and very little of the social requirements of such a position. Affluence, prestige, and social responsibility eventually became more than she could deal with, and she died an unhappy woman, never quite equal to the strange new world so different from her native farm. However, she had a few years of happy toil while Edward was making his vigorous start in business.

Young immigrants were apt to stick together in the melting pot fast coming to a boil in the New York of the seventies. There were thousands of them of every nationality, all pretty much crowded into lower Manhattan. The town was rigidly divided into the rich and the poor. The Grand Hotel, at 31st and Broadway, was the lid on the pot. The territory above it was a different world—a world of elegant victorias, spacious mansions, tree-shaded Fifth Avenue and Central Park, complete with banks and milling Sunday crowds that often made gala occasions of important funerals, saved up for the holiday. Everybody had a good time. The new Grand Central Station stood in the midst of it, a symbol of the affluence that was just then turning the Rockefellers, the Astors, and the Vanderbilts into a legend. Horace Greeley headed the *Tribune* and would soon be put up to run for President against General Grant. The notorious Tweed Ring was on the brink of its downfall at the hands of temporary Reform.

Downtown, things were more boisterous but no less jolly. Since most churches were uptown where the rich could support them with large pew fees, the people spent their Sunday holidays in revelry. Public gardens, beer enclosures, and concert saloons reflected the bibulous but goodhearted habits of the Old Country. The crowds danced, bowled, and drank—mostly drank. It was in this environment that Weston acquired his great love for a tall glass of beer.

For a few cents you could ride for four hours on a horse car and arrive at Coney Island, where the bathing was as good as the voluminous costumes of the day would permit. High, wide and handsome was the life. It cost ten dollars to send a ten-word telegram. There was a subway 295 feet long under Broadway from Warren to Murray Street, but not a single sanitary eating house where good food could be had. The police were an undisciplined mob whose members often changed sides with the many hoodlum gangs that thrived under the waning Boss Tweed and the rising Tammany. Women wore their hair in ringlets and kept their busts from popping out with corsets definitely too small to contain them. They purchased their food at filthy markets which had no iceboxes, at the insistence of barkers who stood out front and raucously proclaimed their wares.

Although Edward was a young man of serious purpose, he did find time occasionally to indulge in the undisciplined merriment of the neighborhood.

Elegant—or at least neat—young men took their girls to the beer halls or Coney Island, or walked them around the waterfront at the Battery; they bought them a small flower now and then and proposed to them quietly in dim-lit boarding house parlors. We should not count it very romantic today, but perhaps romance was then less a matter of glamor than of prospects, and these were, in the girl's eyes, whatever a young man's ambition and imagination could make them. New York was then an environment of little strain and much good-natured fun. The poor had not yet been taught to be sorry for themselves; they probably had more fun than the haughty rich uptown.

Edward had little time for romantic words. He had enormous energy instead. He was short and rather chunky; his eagerness was less in his face than in his rapid movement—a sort of determined push in and out of a room or along a sidewalk, as if somebody had sent for him. Wilhelmina liked that; it gave her a sense of adventure merely to be by his side. There was always a problem to be solved, and never did Edward hesitate or procrastinate. He always knew what he was going to do next. It might not work, but if it didn't, something else would instantly occur to him. He was a pleasant contrast to the ineffectual rivals whom he summarily pushed aside.

Edward never wrote letters if he could help it. Neither did Minnie. So there was no bundle of love letters to hand down to posterity; no record of the courtship; no confidences to friends hinting that he had captured her motherly German heart. There was nothing at all but a marriage certificate.

They were joined in the modest little Methodist Episcopal church on the corner of Duane Street and what was then Seventh Avenue. It was the fifteenth of August, 1871. Brother Ernest loomed over the couple and the minister as he gave the bride away. A handful of friends stood stiffly in the pews and waited for the ceremony to finish. Afterward they all went out and had beers and much revelry, while the happy couple disappeared. The honeymoon may have consisted of one night at the Grand Hotel, or at Coney Island. It may not have included even that, for there was little money to pay for such extravagances and no time to waste on them. The young husband, being the mainstay of a prominent nickel-plating concern, had to get back to his job. The young wife turned to, likewise, determined to make a presentable home out of the dreary two-room flat that Edward had been occupying at 96 Sixth Avenue.

5

All was not well, however, with the American Nickel Plating Company. No sooner had Edward Weston committed himself to the responsibilities of a family than he learned that his employers were in serious difficulties with their competitors, the United Company. These people contended that the plating formula Weston had been using, and improving, was covered in the Adams patent but had not been licensed to him. Now, the owners were suing to recover the patent, claiming infringements and general piracy. To the young scientist, this seemed much more serious than it actually was. He did not yet know that the life of an inventor of his day was about evenly divided between the laboratory and the courtroom. But he was soon to find this out, and when he did, he would become one of the most powerful witnesses ever to enter a patent case.

This particular case did not have time to involve Weston in any other way than to make him mad, for the company fortunes quickly ran onto other difficulties that were at first serious and then fatal. William Belden, as has been said, was a stockbroker by trade, and he saw nickel plating primarily as a market operation. With the rapid growth of the plating art, partly due to Weston's own improvements, nickel itself became very scarce. Not a great deal was being mined then and the price naturally soared. The temptation was too great for Belden and his friends, and they began buying up the metal wherever they could find it, acquiring a stockpile that presently reached the proportions of a corner on the market. They even denied their own plant the use of the vital nickel, preferring to sell it to competitors in small amounts at a large profit.

One day early in 1872, Belden walked into the plant and touched Edward Weston on the shoulder. "Young man," he said. "Wind up the work in hand and draw your pay. We are closing down."

Edward stared at him but made no reply. He was a man of few words, and argument would have been useless. He was well aware of what had been going on. But a scientist couldn't argue with a promoter. They were worlds apart. Besides, he was much too angry, and anger made him even more silent.

So the job ended as it had begun, suddenly and beyond his control. There was nothing for it but to go out and look for work again. This was not a fortunate turn of events. Minnie, long pregnant, gave birth to a son at precisely this moment: the summer of 1872. They named him Walter. Edward insisted that his middle name should be Coleman. He had never forgotten the kindly old doctor who had given him a start in his scientific career.

Weston naturally began by pursuing his connections in the electroplating business. Within a few weeks he had found a berth as technician for the Silver Nickel Plating Company, also in New York. This was a small outfit, which bore a remarkable resemblance to the American Company as Weston had found it the year before. It had been attempting to do silver plating without much success and was struggling against annihilation. In anything but boom times it would have failed long before. Edward took one look at the broken-down shop and immediately turned it into a nickel-plating business.

Characteristically, he was losing interest in his "expert" duties as a plating chemist. What really engaged his attention now was the problem of a better current supply for the tanks. The Smee cells universally used were far from satisfactory—expensive and short-lived. He realized that large current demands could never be met by primary batteries; the dynamo was the logical source of power. But there were no dynamos available in 1872 that could be depended upon. He decided to meet the challenge by designing one of his own.

But this did not solve the immediate problem; it would take too long and be too costly. So he went to work on an improved galvanic battery and soon had an idea for one which he thought a great advance. But a mere idea was a long way from an accomplished fact. It would take money and time for development, exactly as with a dynamo. Just now he had neither to spare. Blocked, he marked time impatiently.

Weston's stay with the Silver Company was not long. As his interest was rapidly shifting to electricity, he quit the job and obtained a position as "consulting expert" to the Commercial Printing Telegraph Company, makers of stock-ticker equipment. It seemed to him that this would be a fine chance to develop his battery ideas. Telegraphy was really the only logical place to use primary batteries. The combination of small current and relatively high voltage required for long lines was well suited to battery output. Edward had dreams of perfecting and patenting his invention and winning acceptance with it in this large industry.

He was disappointed. The company regarded him in about the same light as an organization of today would regard a young laboratory assistant. His days, and sometimes his nights, were filled with routine experimental work on telegraph instruments. He was too much bound to earning a living to dare to be independent.

The luck that had attended his first two years in America seemed to have abandoned him now. He had hardly settled himself in his new job when the company was bought out by a larger one—the Gold and Stock Telegraph Company, which was a subsidiary of Western Union.

In the postwar boom of the 1870's many a wild commercial battle was fought by interests little less than predatory. So much of the scientific domain was brand-new, and so many bright young men were at work inventing the same thing, that companies were formed overnight on the flimsiest of pretexts. It was much like the California gold rush of '49. The gold was there; everyone who could muster an idea or a dollar plunged into the welter of fierce competition, claim jumping, feuding, piracy, and downright hard work, hoping to make his million. There were virtually no laws to protect anybody; a patent was no more than "a license to fight." The few large organizations like Western Union were constantly harassed by infringers, and just as frequently bulldozed their way through the legitimate claims of other people. It was a joyful age of stealing what you could get with one hand while clinging desperately to what was your own with the other.

Though many an honest man invented and patented what he firmly believed to be original, he soon learned that originality did not count so much as an ability to fight. And the small inventor without funds had no chance at all. If he had anything worth stealing it would be gone before the ink was dry on the patent.

Consequently, Edward Weston decided not to work for Western Union. He sincerely believed that if he did, they would soon pry his battery idea out of him and appropriate it.

Late in the fall of 1872 Edward found himself again without work and with little prospect of getting it. He had learned a great deal about how business was conducted; enough, perhaps, to believe that he himself could succeed at a venture of his own. But not without capital. All he had in the world was the few dollars a week he still got for helping Professor Stone at Cooper Union. A conservative young man would have taken what work he could find and waited till he had put something in the bank. But Weston was not conservative. He would rather found a business of his own and be independent than go on marking time on a small salary.

Casting about for a reasonably promising venture, he could find nothing except commercial photography. It was the only thing that he could afford. And so, with some slight protest from his wife, he compressed the family living quarters at 96 Sixth Avenue into the rear of the two rooms he occupied, and turned the front room into a studio. Friends from the Murdock days helped him acquire the necessary camera and supplies. By the time he was ready to open he had used up every penny of savings. The little family prepared to live on what he could make and no more.

He called his place "Weston's Photograph Gallery," and when he was lucky enough to get customers at all, he tried to persuade them to sit for a wet-plate portrait. If they didn't have the money, he made them an old-fashioned tintype instead. Minnie had hung a few cheap drapes about the bare little room so that the subject could pose himself against a reasonably neutral background while the plate took its long "soaking" in the camera. Those were the days before artificial photographic lighting. The subject had to sit still long enough for the daylight to filter in through the dingy windows and capture his fixed smile in the rapidly drying collodion emulsion. Then he waited while the young photographer retired to his tiny dark room and, with the aid of more chemical solutions, discovered whether he had actually caught the portrait or whether the tedious posing and exposing would have to be done over again.

Edward was good at the job; he had a natural instinct for manipulating materials, and a sound knowledge of the photochemical process. His portraits were as good as anybody's in town. This brought him a fair amount of business—enough so that on occasion customers had to wait their turn. To keep them from getting tired and going away, he provided a number of stereoscopes, complete with assorted views of Niagara Falls, handsome flower girls, and the Arc de Triomphe in Paris. This famous old device, held to the face something like a gas mask, displayed two pictures at once, one for each eye, and gave the illusion of three dimensions. Presently they became so popular that the customers began "lifting" the prints, slipping them into their pockets while the proprietor's back was turned. Edward, never at a loss for a strong comeback when justice was concerned, devised a very effective antidote. Across the back of every view card—and sometimes on the front—he wrote in large penscript:

Stolen from Weston's
Photograph Gallery
96 Sixth Ave.

Customers callous enough to display booty around their homes with this accusation written on it proved to be few indeed.

But this was purely a negative success and there was no positive one to accompany it. No matter how much his frugal German *hausfrau* skimped and saved, the family could not exist on the young husband's photographic earnings. Rapidly the supply of money approached the vanishing point.

6

But Edward Weston never stayed down very long. As Christmas of 1872 approached and the photography business faded, he came across a man named George J. Harris, who seemed to have some money and was looking for a good business to invest it in. With a sudden return of enthusiasm, Edward proposed that they start an electroplating company together. Harris knew nothing about it, but the young man's vigor and his obvious knowledge of his subject appealed to him as a fair guarantee of success. He put up the money.

The firm of Harris and Weston was organized late in December, 1872, and opened a modest little shop on Elm Street for general electroplating work in copper, nickel, silver, and gold. Weston presided over the manufacturing end, while Harris took care of the financing and administration and hunted up customers. At Weston's suggestion they had billheads printed that read:

"We guarantee our nickel not to strip or peel."

They had decided to make a specialty of nickel work, using Weston's numerous improvements in the process.

The business thrived, for Weston was as good as his word. His nickel plating was of better quality than any other obtainable in the city. It thrived so well that soon it was necessary to move into

larger quarters. The firm took two adjacent buildings on the corner
of Center and Hester Streets, opposite the old downtown station of
the Harlem Railroad. They employed as many as a dozen men.

No sooner had the change been made than the country was en-
gulfed in the great Panic of 1873. With catastrophic suddenness,
on September 18, the famous banking house of Jay Cooke & Co.,
of Philadelphia closed its doors. This was a signal for general
disaster. Frightened depositors stormed the banks all over the East,
ruining many, temporarily disabling many more. Almost identical
in cause with the great crash of 1929, of which it was a progenitor,
the panic had followed a tremendous postwar boom: overproduc-
tion, overconfidence, wild speculation. Within a few weeks it had
swept the country. The depression which resulted was long and
terrible. Five years later, Henry Ward Beecher was still lecturing
on "Hard Times," assigning the blame for them to the lack of
confidence between man and man. By 1878, 47,000 businesses had
failed, more than a billion of invested capital had been lost.

It was ironic that Edward Weston would have chosen this particular decade to come to America to make his fortune. Thousands of
brilliant people were driven to the wall. That he was not among
them was due partly to his tremendous will to push ahead and
partly to the rise of the new electrical industry. In fact, it was
electricity as much as anything that lit the new lamp of prosperity
as the decade closed.

Harris and Weston hung on somehow during what Beecher called
"the darkest days of America." It was an extraordinary feat for so
new and insecure a concern, due wholly to Weston's courage and
resourcefulness.

He had learned something from his friend Belden: women loved
small shiny objects for self-adornment and would buy such things
in vast quantities, especially if they were silver-plated. Now he
reasoned that if he could change the fashion to nickel plating—
a less expensive and more showy style—he would have an anchor
to windward to ride out the storm. No matter how deep a depression
is, the business of female adornment never quite fails.

His judgment proved entirely correct. Dozens of small feminine
ornaments lent themselves to plating with nickel: shoe buckles, hair

combs, barrettes, buttons, belt buckles, earrings. Soon the plant was almost entirely devoted to turning out these things by the hundreds. He was able to sell them immediately and in wholesale lots to Jewish merchants throughout the city. The virtue of these outlets was that these merchants always had ready money, panic or no panic, and paid for the goods on delivery. The ladies didn't seem to mind the change from silver to nickel; they enjoyed this gesture toward economy.

When survival seemed assured at the beginning of 1874, Weston at last was able to turn his attention to a research he had been contemplating eagerly for two years. This was the invention of a dynamo suitable for supplying current for electroplating. He was convinced that the primary battery was not the logical source of power for this work, even though he himself had plans for a superior chemical cell of his own. Dynamos could be made compact and in any size desired; they would not wear out for many years. So he turned the full force of his inventive ability toward solving the problem.

## 7

We left the history of the dynamo in 1867, when the machine was still a crude affair. The designs of Siemens, Pacinotti, Varley, Wheatstone, and Farmer had more or less defined the future trend toward an efficient arrangement of closed magnetic circuit, cylindrical armature, and a double winding on the field poles to level off the voltage at all electrical loads. Basic principles were understood; it was now necessary to improve the engineering of the device. This Weston undertook to do.

In 1871 Zénobe Théophile Gramme, a Belgian electrician, had begun this work, producing a dynamo with a ring armature similar to Pacinotti's. However, it was not till 1873 that Gramme's machine arrived in America. An important new element in his design, it was found, lay in the fact that he had abandoned the use of a solid cylinder of steel for the armature core, replacing this with a bundle of iron wires fastened parallel to the shaft. The purpose of this was to avoid "eddy currents," generated in the steel by the changing of the magnetic lines of force, an action which diverted considerable of the useful power into waste heat within the armature. By using small iron wires, the eddy current paths were made very short and the stray currents, and hence the resistance loss, were greatly reduced.

Gramme's main contribution, however, was his ability to publicize his designs. He had the backing of many prominent scientists in Paris and was able to put squarely before the scientific world the need of improving dynamo efficiency by careful attention to principles. At this moment the art of electrical *design* was born.

Nevertheless, Gramme's early dynamos were clumsy and inefficient. In fact, as Edward Weston combed the market for an electroplating machine to act as a model he could find nothing remotely suitable. Illogically, this discovery encouraged him. It meant that he could make the advance himself.

Both Gramme and Henry Wilde had claimed that their dynamos could be used for electroplating with better success than batteries. But they had had little opportunity to prove it. The plating fraternity did not want dynamos. They had used batteries for a great many years and clung tightly to the notion that their jealously guarded tricks of manipulating them were responsible for successful results. It was no small undertaking for a young man with relatively little experience to invade this tight corner of manufacture and revolutionize it, at the same time revolutionizing the design of electrical machinery. But that was what he intended to do.

He must first build a dynamo that would actually do electroplating work. The requirements were that rather large, steady currents must be supplied at a closely regulated voltage and at a better over-all efficiency than batteries could do it. It was an uphill job indeed, for many a plating establishment could get along very well with an outlay of twenty dollars or so in primary cells. Nobody could build a dynamo for any such sum as that. His hope, therefore, was a long-range one—to persuade the industry to expand, and in expanding to create a need for machines with an output which no battery could equal.

Weston's first dynamo followed the Gramme design fairly closely, except that it did not use iron wire for the armature core but simply two pole pieces mounted radially on the shaft. It was a pretty cumbersome affair. He got it built in Newark, by the firm that he had previously helped out of chemical difficulties with plating solutions. When it was completed he set it up in his little Elm Street shop and connected it to a small steam engine and boiler. It generated enough current so that actual plating could be done with it.

The machine had two separate armatures on its shaft, revolving within the same pole pieces. One supplied the field current, the other the outside load. The machine was bolted to a heavy table and

An early Weston dynamo.

driven by a belt. To control the output current, Weston inserted resistance in the field circuit, using a rheostat made of German silver wire and wound around the legs of the table. The machine proved to have so much power that he was able to run a primitive arc lamp off the field-exciting armature. In spite of mechanical shortcomings his electrical design had proved to be remarkably good.

So good, in fact, that the Newark people asked if they could copy it. Weston agreed, and when the parts were ready he did the winding for them. This dynamo went into regular service in Newark and was still going strong forty years later when it was destroyed in a fire.

Weston had proved to himself that the dynamo could be applied to electroplating. His own business was already benefiting from its use. But he knew definitely that he could not sell such a crude machine. Consequently, he worked out a second design, using only one armature, and making the whole machine more compact. This was also built for him in Newark, and proved so much better that he decided to standardize on the design and attempt to market it. Twenty of the new dynamos were built before he realized that he still did not have a commercially useful product. The efficiency was still too low and the cost too high to permit it to compete with batteries.

Much time went by, and the Harris and Weston firm did fairly well. With its inventor always on hand to make changes and set up jury rigs, the dynamo gave admirable service; the shop abandoned batteries altogether, except for delicate work in plating with gold. But Edward Weston was determined that his future should lie not in successful electroplating but in the development of electrical machinery. A salable dynamo must somehow be devised.

The only way to balance the high cost of dynamos against the much cheaper battery was to increase their output per dollar of investment to such an extent that they would actually be cheaper than batteries. This meant a sharp rise in efficiency. The only way to achieve that was to make a detailed investigation of the basic theory of electromagnetic machines—something that no one had yet had the patience to do. But Weston had patience to spare, and also a natural instinct for getting to the bottom of a scientific problem. The work he started in dynamo design in the early seventies kept him busy for nearly ten years. Though it was spread out evenly over that period some of it is telescoped here for clarity and convenience.

His first important observation was that the armatures of his dynamos got very hot in service. This heat was a dead loss. It was simple enough to calculate the mechanical input from the steam engine, and the electrical output of the dynamo. Hence its efficiency could be measured with fair accuracy. This turned out to be very poor—less than 40 per cent. The other 60 per cent was thrown away in heat. The large temperature rise prevented the machine from being operated at anywhere near its designed load. A simple improvement, which he introduced at once, was the ventilation of the armature by boring a series of holes through the steel, lengthwise, parallel to the shaft. A stream of cooling air could then be directed through these. The result was the end of overheating. This improved the capacity but had little effect on the efficiency.

The cause of the large loss in the armature was pretty well known—the heating effect of large eddy currents set up in the steel by the rapidly changing magnetic flux. These currents circled about in the steel which offered them short-circuited paths and permitted them to become very large. Only the high resistance of the metal kept them from absorbing all the mechanical power supplied to the armature. The obvious cure was to break up the electrical circuit in the steel. Gramme had done it with some success by using a bundle of iron wires. The same scheme was used in the cores of induction coils. But iron wires were too weak structurally for machines of appreciable power.

Weston's signal contribution here was the breaking up of the armature steel into insulated sections at right angles to the shaft. He realized immediately that the way to do this was to punch out a large number of disks, cut away at the circumference to form the typical two-pole shape, and assemble them with thin spacers of insulating material between, thus cutting down the eddy-current paths to very small dimensions. But he was too poor at the time to afford a large punch press for making such disks. So he made his armature of a single piece of cast iron and cut deep circular grooves in it, concentric with the shaft. The result was much less heating and a considerable improvement in efficiency.

One of the experimental forms of this arrangement is interesting because it was a real forerunner of modern alternating-current machines. Its armature consisted of a wooden drum. Over this Weston slipped a series of flat iron rings, separating each one from its neighbor by a thin ring of stout paper. At one end a larger copper ring was fixed, and at the other a commutator. Instead of windings of wire, he soldered a group of parallel copper strips to the end ring and divided their farther ends equally between the two sections of the commutator, so that each "coil" became a group of heavy conductors in parallel. The similarity of this arrangement to the squirrel-cage induction motor of much later date was quite close, but of course Weston was unable to bury the copper in the iron and so could not get a good magnetic path around the bars. The combination of the large air gap and high cost of manufacture made the machine impractical. He soon went back to the simple two-pole cast-iron armature, similar to the toy motors which we have even today; this was relatively cheap to build and, though inefficient, produced power in reasonable amounts. He had made the opening attack upon eddy current losses and was forced to bide his time till there was money for further experiment.

However, his studies of armature design had pointed the way to a second, and quite as important, advance: the use of the largest possible conductors in the armature circuit, consistent with the voltage required, in order to cut down the resistance losses in the copper. Dynamo theory had grown up as an extension of the theory of batteries, in which it was a fundamental principle that the resistance of the external circuit should be equal to the internal resistance of the battery itself. Inventors had always supposed that the same relationship should be maintained for the dynamo machine. Weston saw that this introduced high resistance losses in the armature at heavy loads and answered no useful purpose. He therefore made the conductors as large as possible for the number of turns needed to produce a given voltage, and was again rewarded with an important increase in efficiency.

He had now established two of the basic principles of design; tests showed him that in theory at least it should be possible to construct a machine for any given service with an efficiency of better than 90 per cent, the losses being confined mainly to friction and such electrical resistance in armature and field as could not be eliminated. There were other losses, such as the hysteresis of the magnetic circuit, which would not be recognized and dealt with for many years yet. However, in general, he had tracked down and overcome the worst shortcomings, and felt that he could produce a dynamo that would be commercially profitable to build and sell.

In accepting the Perkin Medal Award in 1915, Edward Weston harked back to those early days of dynamo making:

I started to design another machine [he said]. I had to reduce the amount of work to a minimum and also the amount of material. Hence, the machine was almost entirely made in a lathe—cylindrical work. There were only two parts . . . which called for a milling machine or plane. After that machine was designed and built and tested we could see that we had something with which we had some possibility of success, but it probably would require quite a lot of hard work to introduce it and get people to buy it. So I designed two small machines: one was about four inches in diameter and about six inches long, to be sold for $65 to the little platers. The other size was about eight inches in diameter and about six inches in length, the armature being somewhat larger, and that was to take care of the pretty good-sized plant and sell for $165.

The remarkable thing about this was that he expected to run a whole electroplating shop with a machine no bigger than an automobile lighting generator of today. It was certainly a tribute to his engineering courage, the more so because he had spent most of his life so far on chemistry. And he succeeded.

This was the beginning of Weston's leadership in the electric power field. He maintained that lead for a decade; his designs were still the best that could be found when they were shown at the Franklin Institute Electrical Exhibit in 1884. By that time he was a successful manufacturer of dynamos, some of which showed an efficiency of better than 90 per cent, well ahead of all his competitors, including Edison.

Just now, in 1873, it was almost impossible to sell a dynamo, no matter how good it was.

Some of the difficulties we encountered were very amusing. First, . . . long-time plating. The platers got ready during the day and ran the baths at night so there was on an average twelve to fourteen hours of plating. Of course, that could not be done with a machine because it would require the steam power all night. Necessarily, we had to change their solutions and methods in order to coat as thickly in about two and a half to three and a half hours as had been done in twelve to fourteen hours. And solutions were a tender subject. Then, the operators themselves did not like the machine for they regarded their skillful manipulation of the batteries as part of their stock in trade.

Again, the matter of price was a serious stumbling block. He persuaded a Mr. Strickland of Albany to try out a dynamo in his silver-plating works. Strickland was quite annoying about it, for although he permitted a machine to be installed, he gave little cooperation and merely took the newfangled thing on trial, no money down.

Weston spent many days getting the plant changed over, with scant help from anybody. At the end of a month the plater paid for the dynamo and kept it. He was convinced. "You tell that fellow Weston," he remarked to a mutual friend, "that I did everything in the world to insult him when he was trying to do me a favor."

This is often the way of great inventions. The people who ought to do most to support them usually go out of their way to ignore them and cast doubts upon the men who make them. At least, that was the way in those days; now, a big invention does not even reach the public till millions have been spent on its development and its performance can be guaranteed. No doubt the nineteenth century was right in its reluctance; the public itself was the laboratory in which every invention was developed. It had to stand for some pretty hard knocks and not a few expensive disappointments.

However, Edward Weston was one of those who really had something to give, and he knew it. Within a year or two his plating dynamos had "caught on" so well that he had begun to devote most of his time to them.

8

The period from 1873 to 1875 was one of reasonable prosperity for Weston, and there was no more scraping to find money for the next meal for his family. The plating business kept growing, and he was assured of selling as many dynamos as he could get built, which was not very many.

But Weston's mind was broad enough to embrace more than one project at a time. Thus, in the midst of his close attention to dynamo design he made a second attempt to improve the quality of nickel plating—and succeeded. The malleable nickel which had eluded him in 1871 yielded to capture now.

His victory resulted purely from his ability to investigate to the root of a matter and *really* know what it was about. In this case he was working in a branch of chemistry—electroplating—which was full of notions and taboos, based partly on ignorance and partly on rule of thumb. Some of these notions were embodied in the Adams patent, on which most platers relied for their methods. One of them in particular was that the single salts of nickel could

not be used for the plating solution—that is, nickel chloride, sulphate, and so on. The same rule forbade the use of the double
sulfate of nickel and potassium, or any other combination of nickel
and an alkali metal. If you worked with the alkalis, you deposited
the more active metal on the work and got no nickel plating at all.
If you tried the single salts you would first get a good nickel coating
but soon destroy it with an added layer of nickel hydroxide, a dirty,
green deposit that was familiar in every plating establishment when
depositing was done too fast.

These rules seemed all wrong to Weston. He knew that the
alkali metals could never plate out in metallic form, for they were
too active. They would immediately recombine with water to form
hydroxides in solution. As for the green hydroxide deposit, there
was no doubt of its existence, but only a question as to how it got
there and whether it was unavoidable. The fact that the U.S. Patent
Office had backed up Adams in these contentions and had given him
a patent to prove it, meant nothing to the young chemist. He wanted
to find out what actually did happen and then remedy it.

It seemed a simple matter to him, now, to prepare some very
pure solutions in which all the ingredients were under close control
and to demonstrate what the chemical reactions really were. Constructing a miniature electroplating tank he filled it with a solution
of the single salt, nickel sulphate, then introduced electrodes of
copper and nickel, and passed current through it. At first the nickel
plated out on the copper perfectly, then began to deposit the characteristic green hydroxide. Weston tested the solution and found
that, while it had at first been acid, it was now alkaline. He made
it acid again by the addition of a little sulphuric acid, and the green
scum instantly disappeared. This, then, was the real explanation. It
was not the use of the single nickel salt that caused the trouble, as
Adams contended, but the preponderance of nickel hydroxide generated in the solution by the chemical transfer during plating. By
keeping the bath always acidulous, Weston showed that the single
nickel salts—chloride, bromide, sulphate, or iodide—would all produce good plating. Moreover, a great deal smoother and finer plate
could be deposited, and much faster than by the old method.

Then came the crucial test:

Not satisfied with this I prepared extraordinarily pure nickel, taking great precautions to exclude every trace of potash, soda, alumina and lime, and I found that the solution acted exactly as did my first solution and the commercial sort. This led to the invention of a nickel anode and a new solution that gave me my really first great start.

Standard anodes were then made of cast nickel. Weston now introduced a new type, composed of pure nickel grains mixed with powdered carbon and a binder of pitch (later he used molasses), all compacted into a block by hydraulic pressure. With this, and a solution kept acidified with weak boric acid, he was able to produce nickel plating that was as soft and smooth as silver, that could be rolled or hammered, and that did not flake or chip off. He had reached his intended goal.

After a year of successful use, he patented the anode. It was his first patent, obtained in the summer of 1875, and became basic in the electroplating industry forthwith.

Three years later he took out another patent, this time on the use of the single nickel salt with boric acid added. Again he had produced a basic change in the art. But this time, he and his patent attorney slipped. He should have written "a mild acid" in place of "boric." Eventually, smart competitors substituted acetic acid and were able to benefit from Weston's invention without the annoyance of paying him royalties.

### 9

The triumph in electroplating chemistry, it is true, led to patents and the enviable position of having caused a revolution in the industry. But it was clouded by continual trouble, which caused a serious drain on Weston's time and patience and in fact threatened the very existence of his new venture. No sooner had Harris and Weston formed their partnership than they fell heir to the lawsuit which the United Nickel Company had originally brought against the American Nickel Plating Company. But now the complaint had broadened from a simple action to recover the use of the Adams patents from a licensee, to a full-fledged infringement action which sought to put Harris and Weston out of business.

Although at that time patents were granted in a few weeks after applications were filed, infringement suits were luxuries of a different order. They often went on for years. The action against Weston, argued before the U.S. Circuit Court for the Southern District of New York, was not finally settled until October, 1878. The plaintiffs won, proving infringement of two claims of the Adams patent. But the delay was fortunate, for by that time the young inventor was well out of the plating business and was successful enough in dynamo manufacture to have money to pay the piper.

This first patent suit was a bitter experience to Weston. But it was a valuable introduction into a field which he subsequently came to love, because it exactly suited his belligerent nature. It showed him the kind of competition he was up against and would have to meet all his life. In an art as new as applied electricity it was to be a downright battle for supremacy, based on the simplest fundamentals, evident to all. It was to be a case of one man's ingenuity against another's. There was no organized research then to supply a great variety of new principles on which patents could be soundly based. Technical knowledge was so scant that there was no room as yet for patents to be well differentiated.

But that bothered no one. In fact, inventors seemed to enjoy the risks immensely. We speak with horror today of "cutthroat" competition. In those times they lived and thrived on nothing else, as eager for the struggle as a group of jockeys pounding along a narrow track, constantly fouling each other to gain an inch of advantage on the turns.

In electroplating, in dynamo design, in electric arc lighting, there was one set of fundamental scientific facts from which every inventor must start, and the result was that everybody invented approximately the same thing, hastily patented it, and rushed into manufacture, hoping to sell as many units as possible before the inevitable infringement suit started.

Although Weston's experiments had shown the Adams patent claims to be unsound chemically, the lawyers did such a fine job of argument, invective, and sarcasm that the bewildered judge found for the plaintiffs. In establishing the genius of Dr. Adams, Edward N. Dickerson, the chief counsel for the complainant, described an occasion when the inventor had saved a plater whose solutions wouldn't work:

The Remington patent (another alleged infringement) was as comprehensive as the heavens. It was a patent for anything nickel-plated. They could not make it work; and they accidentally came in contact with Dr. Adams and put him in there to see what he could do. . . . Adams went in there and made the solution and it was then that the hinges . . . were plated. . . . Mrs. Peabody, being a Spiritualist, fell into a trance, to find out how Adams did the plating, and it was revealed to her that it was done by means of skunk's cabbage; and so Remington got skunk's cabbage and put it into his solution to make it plate. These were the people who claimed to have a patent for the successful art of nickel plating. . . .

And so on, the intention being to indicate that anybody except Adams who tried electroplating was either an alchemist or a pirate.

By his decision the judge admitted that this was so.

Seeing how much nonsense enjoyed the dignity of acceptance in court, Weston determined to become an expert in the giving of testimony, hoping to bring some sanity into so preposterous a situation. It was apparent that neither the lawyers nor the judges knew anything about science. It ought to be easy to confound them by producing a little of the truth. In subsequent years he did just this, and became a pioneer in raising the level of the typical patent suit from the ridiculous to a reasonably competent technical routine in which justice could be fairly secured. He was so successful, indeed, that litigants sought him again and again for his professional testimony. It became a byword in civil court that if Edward Weston was to testify, the opponents had best look to their case.

But only Weston himself could know how bitter had been that first defeat or how cruel the lesson it had taught.

In 1874, with the case in full swing, Harris signified that he would like to withdraw from the business. His retirement was only partial, but he ceased to be of any real use. Weston found another partner, a Mr. Warner, and the firm name was changed to Warner and Weston. But the new blood did not have much color; Warner played along but he did not do much work, especially in court. Weston found himself virtually running a one-man concern. The load was too great. The once profitable business was close to ruin. Yet he honored his obligations to his partners and put up a valiant battle to guard their interests as well as his own.

How serious was the situation is shown by one of his rare letters, written to a machinist in Newark who was helping him to build his early plating dynamos.

182 Centre St.
Jan. 30th, 1874

Friend Theberath:

I do not see how I can get over to Newark to fix up the machine. You know how I have neglected my business for the last year and 10 months on account of this terrible law suit. The consequence is that our business is almost ruined and we find it difficult to make ends meet. . . . You see I am indeed in a peculiarly distressing position. My duty to my partners calling for my time in the business; and my duty to you, who has done me so many kindnesses, and to whom I am deeply obligated, calling upon me to put the machine in such a position that it can be placed upon the market.

Although I am extremely poor and find it difficult to get along with the salary I am getting from the nickel business, and really wish I was free, yet I cannot, even though I do suffer, conscientiously leave the business. I must as an honest man stick to it and struggle to carry it through to a successful issue.

He could not, he felt, spend any time at all in Newark helping Theberath with the dynamo.

Now, this is what I propose. Suppose you send over every machine to me to wind, test and run. I mean to say, suppose I take charge of the construction of the machine so far as relates to the electrical branch of the business; and you give me the machines finished so far as the machinist's work is concerned. Now I think that by working late nights I can do it and return them to you finished and ready for sale.

It was one of those typical struggles where a talented inventor had tied himself up so tightly with the products of one talent that he was prevented from making good with the fruits of another and greater one.

Long before the case was settled, or gave promise of ever being settled, Weston had resolved to quit the nickel business altogether. He was only waiting for the moment when his obligations should lighten enough to let him quit with honor. This moment came at last, in 1875, when Harris and he quarreled. Harris had never been of much account beyond the initial—and essential—office of furnishing the capital to start the plating venture. He was less and less willing to be involved now that the burdensome patent suit was taking more time than the business itself. So he quietly removed himself. Warner did the same. There was no dissolution of the firm; Weston was simply left "holding the bag."

Gathering his notes together he decided to apply for a patent on the nickel anode. It was his invention alone; he felt no qualms about taking it for himself. With the help of a patent attorney he wrote the thing up and sent it to Washington.

Then Edward Weston packed up his family and moved to Newark, New Jersey.

# PART THREE

# The Fighter

---

I

Edward Weston applied for his first patent on July 10, 1875, covering his invention of the compressed nickel anode. It was granted to him on August 3. Today this would be impossible, for more than seven hundred examiners in the Patent Office are well over two years behind in their work. But in 1875 things moved with dispatch. There were not many inventions being made.

The anode patent alone would have been of little use to him, had it not been for a chain of fortunate circumstances that was slowly forging itself in his life. His decision to move out of New York and settle in Newark was of the same sort that had prompted him to undertake his own photographic studio—a long gamble, the principal prize being independence. He was at heart a pioneer; the moment an undertaking turned routine he got restless and wanted a change. Usually that change involved a great risk, but this held no terrors for Weston. He knew there would always be new experimental territory to move into, especially in electricity.

So, he courageously picked up his home in July of 1875 and moved it to a house on Eighth Avenue in Newark. He had resolved to devote his entire time to the building of dynamos, with the help of his friends the Theberath brothers and their little machine shop.

That first year in New Jersey was a tough one and he was never very far from poverty. Only a very few of his plating dynamos were selling, for they were so expensive that only the largest shops could afford them. Nevertheless, he was beginning to be known in the industry as an expert, and there was a definite interest in switching from batteries to dynamos. It could not be denied that his machines worked and had numerous advantages over batteries. Many people

59

were watching him with attention, to see whether he could bring the price down to a competitive figure.

Among Weston's large customers was Eberhard Faber, the pencil manufacturer. Faber was also turning out a large quantity of pens, which he plated with copper or gold by means of batteries. He now wrote Weston to say that his plating solutions were not working very well, and invited him to investigate the trouble. Weston made a trip to the Faber plant, which was in Camden, N. J., and brought back a sample of the plating solution for test. He soon found what the trouble was—the same old matter of alkalinity—and made a second trip to Camden to put it right. By the time he had made several visits he had the Faber plating baths in fine order, doing a grade of work they had never been able to do before. He now thought it time to suggest the purchase of a dynamo. In April, 1876, Mr. Faber accepted the suggestion and asked him to supply a machine as soon as he could.

Evidently (to judge by the few letters that are preserved in regard to the matter), Weston did not have or could not produce a dynamo that pleased Mr. Faber. For the next five months he was unable to deliver any machine at all. "When may I expect you to carry out your agreement in regard to gilding?" wrote the manufacturer tersely. "I am anxious to proceed at once." And, somewhat later, after a machine had finally been installed, "The gilding is done so poorly that I am not able to use the goods at all. Will you please call at my office (in New York) at your earliest convenience?"

The poor inventor was harassed with more complications than he could manage. When there was a choice between his obligations to his scientific work and his dealing with customers, he took science and let the customers wait. But in the end, Faber was pacified, as most people were who came in contact with Edward Weston's dynamic personality. Meekly he joined the rest of the buying public who were forced to act as guinea pigs at this early stage of engineering development.

Weston clinched the matter by selling him a considerable number of his patented nickel anodes, also.

Gradually, as 1875 ended and '76 began, he started to make dynamo sales rather consistently. His customers included a stove

The energetic young inventor.

company, the Stanley Lock works, a number of tableware manufacturers, and a sewing machine company, all of them interested in doing their own nickel plating of component parts. One of the first firms to show real enthusiasm was a large metal novelty establishment in Newark: Stevens, Roberts and Havell, to whom he sold a small machine in October, 1875. This customer had come to his attention in an interesting way while he was still struggling with misfortune in New York.

The United Nickel Company had not been content to bring suit against Weston's little company alone, but had included everybody within reach, hoping that by cutting off access to the Adams patents on all sides it would become dominant in the plating field. Stevens, Roberts and Havell were among the court victims of this high-handed attempt and one day found themselves in court with Weston as a codefendant. When the young man's turn came to speak he leaped up and defended himself so ably that the firm's lawyers were greatly impressed and told their employers about him. Shortly Stevens sought him out and finding that he did not have the funds to hire a lawyer, offered to lend him his own. Weston accepted quickly.

It was a fortunate moment for the young inventor, for it gave him adequate legal help and a loyal friend. Shortly, it also provided him with a new customer.

The Theberath brothers, Charles and Jacob, were also good friends of Stevens, especially the former, who handled the business end of his small firm. Charles soon became a strong champion of Weston and a useful contact man between the two. It was this friendly aid that pulled Weston through his first real business crisis. The relationship had begun in 1874 and the Theberaths and Weston were quickly on intimate terms, their families seeing a good deal of each other socially.

> Friend Weston: [Charles wrote in October, 1874]
> Just this minute I received your favor of the 30th, noticing all the contents. I feel with you. Mr. Stevens has sent you some money last Tuesday. I hope you have received it by this time. Let me know how much he sent you and if you are in need of more, telegraph to me at once and I will see him. Mr. Stevens,

Mr. Van Winkle and myself went around last Monday and raised enough money to see you through. If you have not received enough from Mr. Stevens this week let me know at once and more will come. Do not get discouraged. We will stand by you, and not only that. We will do what we can for you afterwards when you get through with this trouble. . . .

The situation was that Stevens and Van Winkle were business men of substance in the New Jersey metropolis. The Theberaths had done good work for them and had earned their respect and support. Now Weston came into the picture with a remarkable invention which the machine shop had decided to manufacture in a small way. But the young man was on the point of being swallowed up by litigation, bringing ruin on himself and considerable loss to the partners. It was natural that Stevens and his friends should want to save this talented inventor with a view to making a profitable deal all round. Hence the loan and the great solicitude shown in the letter.

Most of this had happened in 1874. In fact, it was largely at Stevens' urging that Weston took the long chance in moving to Newark the following year. The first thing he did there was to make arrangements for the manufacture of his nickel anode by Stevens' firm. The venture seemed like a slender hope; nevertheless it definitely removed Weston from the danger of starvation.

2

The year 1876 was a banner year for Weston. As it began he was hard at work on basic improvements in his dynamo machine. Since the Theberath shop was extremely small—too small for experimental work of any kind—he set up a "laboratory" in his own house. It was a little hard for Minnie to manage this. The house was none too large and Edward insisted on devoting the whole top floor to the clutter and perpetual mess of shop work, whose inevitable shavings and metal splinters sifted down the stairs and had to be swept up constantly. This may have been an entering wedge between them; at any rate it was the beginning of a dislike which she conceived for the whole art of invention and manufacture.

Weston's marriage, while it was a happy one at this stage, was taking less and less of his attention. His mind was so completely engrossed with his inventions, and every waking moment so filled with work, that he had already begun to let his social activities languish. His relationship with his wife was increasingly impersonal. Here were the seeds of discontent, rapidly sprouting for them both. Letters to him from the Theberaths, during his absence on business, constantly referred to visits made to his home to see how his wife and child were getting on. These loyal friends never failed to mention her charm. But if Weston was worried about the welfare of his family while he was away, preoccupation with science prevented the expression of solicitude immediately he returned.

He had a small lathe which he ran by foot power, and a few hand tools. That was all he could afford. And yet, early in 1876, he produced in this attic room the first really significant advance in dynamo design since Siemens had invented the shuttle armature. This was the multipolar machine, using a cylindrical frame—essentially the arrangement in use today. Up to that time all the world had clung to the old concept of a "magneto-electric" machine based on the horseshoe permanent magnet, with one north pole and one south in the field magnetic circuit, and a similar pair of poles in the armature. This gave one rise and fall of induced voltage for each half revolution, and required a two-section commutator to produce current flow in one direction. Edward Weston reasoned that there was too much of the circle of revolution during which the armature coils were not passing opposite field poles and hence were doing no work. He therefore proposed to multiply the number of field poles until the gaps between them were only large enough to prevent magnetic flux from leaking directly from pole to pole without passing through the cores of the armature coils. He arranged the poles symmetrically, alternately north and south, putting a corresponding number of poles on the armature. Another great advance in design suggested itself immediately: the use of a cylindrical steel shell around the outside of the field poles, joining them all together, giving them good mechanical support, and at the same time providing a short and ample magnetic path.

This arrangement was directly contrary to the construction then held to be necessary. Just as the first automobiles built would look exactly like carriages, with only the horse removed, so the first dynamos were patterned after the horseshoe magnet. It was believed that a long loop of steel was needed in order to "concentrate" the flux at the pole tips. It occurred to no one that the shortest possible magnetic circuit would be the most efficient. To no one, that is, except Weston. This belief persisted for years after this; in 1881 Edison insisted on designing his first electric light machines with towering pole pieces, and only cut them down when the art of dynamo design became firmly based on theory. Weston, not fully comprehending the theory in 1876, courageously put forward his cylindrical dynamo because it seemed like common sense. He was going to do that all his life. And for that reason his early dynamos were the most efficient that could be had.

On April 4, 1876, he applied for a patent on the multipolar cylindrical construction; the patent was granted in July.

In the meantime a great event had taken place—the breathtaking Centennial at Philadelphia. America was showing the world what it had done in the arts in its first hundred years. In gigantic Machinery Hall, overlooking the Schuylkill River, the Centennial had assembled every type of appliance that American ingenuity had devised, and sparsely sprinkled them with exhibits of similar wares from foreign countries. The Gargantuan Corliss steam engine, with its thirty-ton flywheel, dominated the scene and attracted most attention. But history was being made on that floor. In an obscure corner a handfull of small electric arc lamps were flickering on, in a valiant and unbelievable effort to light the world by electricity. These lamps were supplied, not by batteries, but by dynamos. And one of the three machines being shown was a dynamo that Weston had hastily built in the Theberath's shop and set up himself in the earnest hope that it would not be entirely overlooked.

Whether it was or not will never be known. At the grand award of prizes, on September 27, no less a celebrity than Sir William Thomson headed the committee of judges. Weston got nothing. He was overshadowed completely by the fame of Gramme and Professor Farmer. Ironically, the Newark firm of Condit, Hanson and

Company received an award for excellent electroplating materials. In less than a year, these materials would be entirely outmoded and replaced by the inventions of this still obscure Englishman.

3

STEVENS, ROBERTS & HAVELL

Manufacturers of Steel, Brass and Enamelled

FANCY                    GOODS

Ladies' Dress Trimmings, Belt Clasps & Buckles,
Steel and Fancy Metal Buttons, Button Hooks & Shoe Buckles,
Trunk & Bag Trimmings, Brass and Steel Escutcheon Pins,
Steel Springs, Thurber's Anti-Friction Metal,
Men's, Boys' & Ladies' Hat Slides, Buckles and Ornaments

284 & 286 Washington Street,                    Newark, N. J.

Thus went the letterhead on which Frederick Stevens wrote to Weston soon after his disappointing failure to receive recognition at Philadelphia in September, 1876. It was one of the most important letters Weston ever got, for it opened the door to his future in electrical engineering. It is amusing, perhaps, that a manufacturer of women's novelties and metal odds and ends should have been so important an agent. Partly, it is explained by the fact that Stevens had retired and was giving his thought and his money to promoting worthy new enterprises.

What his letter proposed was that the young inventor join the firm and open a new manufacturing department exclusively for the making of Weston plating machines. The contract was signed on September 10, 1876, and set Edward Weston up in a single small room in the factory on Washington Street. The document provided that Roberts and Havell were to receive a half interest in the nickel anode patent and also in the patent covering the multipolar dynamo. Profits, if there should be any, were to go three quarters to the company and one quarter to Weston. The young man was to receive a salary of sixteen dollars a week for devoting half his time to the dynamo business.

Weston's inventive career was launched at last, with such backing

as any young scientist might have envied. The arrangement eliminated his good friends the Theberaths, and they were sorry to see
him go. But their little shop was plainly inadequate. The dawn of
electric power development was coming, and he needed resources,
both financial and mechanical, to help him meet the fierce competition soon to spring up on every side.

Not only did the arrangement promise Weston commercial success, but a chance to do real research work as well—to have at his
elbow skilled mechanics who could turn out model after model as
fast as he conceived them. Today this is a routine requirement in any
industry. Then, for an inventor to be taken seriously by substantial
businessmen was a privilege that hardly anybody but the fabulous
Mr. Edison could command.

The one small shop in the basement of the Washington Street
plant soon grew to two, and Weston had "his room" to himself.

Out of it came most of the significant developments in dynamo
efficiency already mentioned. So far as Roberts and Havell were concerned, he was to design and build dynamos for the electroplating
and electrotyping industries. But Weston was beginning to see a
future for the dynamo in electric lighting, and even in electric motive
power for machinery. He wanted to expand as fast as possible. He
planned to experiment on dynamos in general, and soon on arc
lamps and lighting systems as well.

From the start his relationship with the heads of the firm was
most cordial, particularly with George Havell. Weston and the
junior partner saw a great deal of each other. They lived only two
doors from each other on Eighth Avenue, and "ran in" constantly.
In everything but name Weston was soon a partner in the firm.

Wisely, the company kept the new dynamo business entirely
separate from its other activities, and in this way prevented it from
being submerged in other, more proven work. The plating machine
began to catch on rather startlingly. They were now selling every
dynamo they could build, which, it must be admitted, was not very
many, judging by modern standards. They were even selling a few
in Europe.

The reasons for the Weston dynamo's quick popularity were

simplicity and low cost. At first the inventor wisely postponed refinements in design and efficiency. The novelty and convenience of
electric power in real quantity—quantity larger than any battery
could supply—was enough, without too close attention to the cost
of the steam power to produce it. The machines were of the simple
two-pole type, with an occasional four- or six-pole machine when
a very large size was ordered.

Meanwhile, Edward Weston put in long hours in his new laboratory. Aside from the general problem of improving dynamo efficiency, he was faced with a new and serious situation that arose
from the substitution of dynamos for batteries in electroplating
work. Customers complained that the machines frequently reversed
themselves and *unplated* partially plated work; that is, they actually
sent current through the electroplating baths in the wrong direction
after making a correct start. Weston made a quick study of the
difficulty and soon saw what was the matter.

When a new dynamo was first set up for test its field coils were
given a "shot" of outside current to magnetize the pole pieces. This
immediately started the machine to generating a voltage of its own,
which in turn magnetized the field to full strength through the shunt
winding and established its polarity. The field poles now retained
a permanent residual magnetism—enough to build up an initial
voltage whenever the machine was run. In service on a plating circuit it would deliver electrolyzing current in the right direction so
long as the terminals were properly connected and so long as the
machine kept on running. But when it was stopped for any reason
during the process a critical situation arose. The electrodes of dissimilar metals, being immersed in the electrolyte, immediately
"polarized" and produced a voltage of their own in opposition to
that of the dynamo circuit. This polarization lasted only a few
minutes and could be eliminated by briefly short-circuiting the bath.
But in slowing down, the dynamo voltage would drop off and
presently become less than the polarization potential. Immediately,
a current would flow out through the dynamo and through its field
circuit, in the reverse of normal direction, wiping out the residual
magnetism and setting up a field of the wrong polarity. When the
machine was again started, it would have changed polarity itself

and would actually supply current in the wrong direction, so that the unplating action would begin.

A similar difficulty would arise if a properly magnetized machine were connected to a bath before its generated voltage was high enough to overcome the bath's own voltage. Either way, reverse magnetization ensued, ruined the electrolyte, spoiled the work, and put the dynamo out of commission until it could be remagnetized in the right polarity again.

A simple disconnecting switch would obviate this trouble, provided that it was never closed unless the dynamo voltage was higher than the minimum required to prevent reverse current flowing. But it was not possible to rely upon the workmen in a plating plant to know this. One mistake would spoil everything; there were neither instruments nor relays to protect the circuits and warn the operator of the dangerous condition. Hence the growing list of complaints, all of which blamed Weston for selling dynamos that were unreliable. Presumably it was this trouble that had made Eberhard Faber so furious.

Weston had to solve the difficulty immediately and permanently. So he developed a regulator that would automatically cut the dynamo out of circuit unless it was rotating above a certain speed. The device was a centrifugal switch, consisting of a cup of mercury revolved by a belt from the dynamo shaft. Contact with a center electrode was broken only when the pool of mercury whirled fast enough to climb the walls of the cup. Weston used this on all his machines for short-circuiting the plating bath and dynamo and hence rendering them mutually harmless. This arrangement was possible only because the electrical losses in the machine were so large that serious short-circuit currents could not build up.

This cutout worked very well indeed. Weston patented it on October 3, 1876, shortly after joining the Newark firm. Crude as the device was, it remained a stand-by for a considerable time, effectively ending the reverse-current trouble and the customers' complaints. It was a good many years before the modern electromagnetic relay, such as we have on automobiles, was invented.

The method of short-circuiting was not satisfactory for large plating dynamos, since they could not be started under so heavy an electrical load without slipping their driving belts off. So Weston joined with Edward E. Quimby, an attorney, in patenting an improved mercury regulator which established contact only when it was revolving fast enough. This "compound switch" also short-circuited the plating tank as it opened the dynamo circuit, so that the polarization currents could discharge themselves and leave the electrodes in a neutral condition for further plating.

## 4

Although it was Edward Weston's intention to leave the plating field eventually, he made one more electrochemical invention in this period which had a profound effect on the mechanical arts. This was his pioneer work in the electrolytic refining of metals, notably copper, silver, and gold. In making the Perkin Medal Award in 1915, Dr. Leo H. Baekeland gave Weston the credit for pioneering this important art in America.

At this time [1877–8] attempts had already been made for the commercial refining of copper by means of the electric current. But this subject was then in its first clumsy period, far removed from the importance it has attained now among modern American industries. Here, again, Weston brought order and method where chaos had reigned. His careful laboratory observations, harnessed by his keen reasoning intellect, established the true principles on which economic, industrial, electrolytic-copper refining could be carried out.

Professor James Douglas, who was the country's foremost metallurgical authority at this time, and who first experimented with electrolytic refining on a big scale for the copper industry, went to Weston for advice and help. "I suppose," he said, "that I may claim the merit of making in this country the first electrolytic copper by the ton, but the merit is really due Weston, who, in this and innumerable other instances has concealed his interested work for his favorite science and pursuits under a thick veil of modesty and generosity."

This double tribute to Weston was typical. No one ever had to fear that the young Englishman would be predatory or try to claim for himself an improvement which was made by another, even though his advice was a determining factor.

Baekeland goes on:

The whole problem of electrolytic refining, when Weston took it up, was hampered by many wrong conceptions. One of them was that a given horse-power could deposit only a maximum weight of copper, regardless of cathode or anode surface. This fallacious opinion was considered almost an axiom until Weston showed clearly the way of increasing the amount of copper deposited per electrical horsepower by increasing the number and size of vats and their electrodes, connecting his vats in a combination of series and multiple, the only limit to this arrangement being the added interest and capital and depreciation on the increased cost of more vats and electrodes, in relation to the cost of horsepower for driving the dynamos.

Copper refining—that is, the separation of pure copper from gold, silver, and base metals after concentration of the ores by roasting— soon came to be an important branch of the electrical art. Without the very high purity which was only possible through electrolysis, the millions of tons of the red metal used by the electric power industry could not have been made into good enough conductors to permit efficient machines and apparatus to be developed. Thus Weston, though he made no patent claims for it, became one of the fathers of the electrical age in a field not primarily his own.

In the matter of taking credit Weston was properly modest all his life. But he was never retiring or faint of heart. As this first period of his prosperity began, he was already far different from the uncertain youth who had landed at the Battery in 1870. Now he had become aggressive, self-confident, and even unapproachable. He abhorred writing letters, and never did so unless it was an absolute necessity. Time and again his files yield communications from his associates, begging, even threatening him with suits if he did not answer them or keep an arranged appointment. His conduct often seemed willful to his friends and partners; they did not fully under-stand that any interest that he took up immediately became a rage with him and blotted out everything else. His mind had as many tracks to it as a railroad yard, but he never proceeded on more than one track at a time, and this at the pace of the fastest express train.

It must have been a trying job for his patent attorney to hold Weston in line. Exasperated, Edward E. Quimby once wrote:

Dear Weston:

Why don't you send me memorandum of particulars about tele-
graphing apparatus as you promised? Or have you instructed
somebody else to prosecute for patent?

I expect to meet next week the parties with whom I should
negotiate for the sale of the invention.

I tried to telephone you Sunday but they said they could get
no reply from your house.

Answer immediately.

Yours truly,

E. E. Quimby

It is hard for us to realize now, in the midst of world decadence,
what tremendous energy and singleness of purpose was the gift
of the men who established our modern easy life. Hours, salary, and
health meant nothing to them so long as they could work at the
thing they loved to do.

5

The reason for Weston's aloofness as 1877 began, was not hard
to find. He was involved in a very successful and exciting venture
indeed. By May of that year Roberts and Havell had sold more than
one hundred dynamos for electroplating, and the demand was growing daily. The business, in fact, had outgrown the tiny shop which
was its incubator on Washington Street, Newark. So, in June of that
year the firm decided to organize a separate company solely for
making electrical apparatus. On June 10, the Weston Dynamo Electric Machine Company began existence, duly incorporated in New
Jersey. A capital of $200,000 was authorized, and many prominent
men of Newark immediately subscribed, although stock was not
issued for the full amount at first. The president of the new concern
was Abraham Van Winkle, of a prominent platers' supply house,
and long a friend of the inventor. The treasurership was taken by
James Roberts, of the parent firm, and Edward Weston became
secretary and general manager. After exactly seven years in this
country, the young Englishman had a full-fledged business under his
own name, and under his own charge as well, for he was the brains

and the driving force of the organization. Success now was almost wholly in his own hands.

In those days new companies rarely built themselves new plants as they do today, but took such buildings as the market afforded and made them over to suit their work. The only quarters available in the vicinity of Roberts and Havell was an empty Jewish synagogue, also on Washington Street. This they took over, with almost no alterations, and began operating it as a dynamo factory. It was the first electrical machinery plant in America.

Everybody called it "The Church." Fortunately, it had not been built for worship originally, and so was easily adaptable to its new duties. Actual manufacturing was begun on the fairly spacious second floor, while the downstairs portion was divided up into tiny offices and a storeroom. After a few weeks as the presiding genius over this modest little domain, Weston insisted upon moving his experimental work into separate quarters, so that he might proceed without interruption from manufacturing problems. The building next door, being empty also, was hired for the purpose, and his entire equipment was moved into it, including most of the primitive machinery and the few tools he had gathered at home. It was a modest layout indeed, by any modern standard, but a real laboratory for him for the first time in his life. The most important thing it had was steam power, so that he could actually test his improved machines as fast as he invented and built them.

Production of plating dynamos continued at the old plant at full blast until the new one was ready, then proceeded at an ever-increasing pace in "The Church." Here, also, Weston began turning out his patent nickel anodes, as well as chemical salts for his improved plating solutions, and numerous products for cleaning and polishing the work. The company was a complete source of supply for everything that an electroplater of nickel, gold, and silver might need. It was now one of the leading manufacturers in the field. Van Winkle's own firm, Condit, Hanson & Van Winkle, were appointed as sole agents for the distribution of the products. Although they had long been in the electroplating supply business themselves, there seems to have been no competition. Edward Weston's products represented a new era. On the strength of them the Van Winkle firm survived, and is still in business in New Jersey today.

By mid-1877 the Weston dynamo had thoroughly "caught on" and was beginning to drive the primary battery out of the industry. A very good reason for this was that the inventor refused to be satisfied with the routine sales efforts of his agents and insisted on going on the road himself. He had plenty of precedent for this, for every inventor who hoped to make headway at all had to tackle his sales problems in person. Nobody else appreciated the merits of his inventions well enough to overcome the fierce competition on every hand. It was long before the days of the high-powered sales department. An inventor was an individual who survived or fell strictly by the exercise of his wits, in every branch of the business.

One of the continuing strongholds of the primary plating battery was in New England, among the silversmiths. These specialists believed that high-quality work could only be done by the skillful manipulation of battery current at the hands of lifelong experts. Then, as now, Connecticut was a leader in this field. One of the larger firms was then depositing as much as two-and-a-half tons of silver every year. Weston made up his mind to invade the Nutmeg State and make it see the light.

Mr. Edward F. Weston, the inventor's younger son, born about this time, has given an amusing description of his father's energetic sales methods, in a recent speech. It runs as follows:

The method of sales pursued consisted of loading a batch of new machines on a freight car and shipping it to a central point, such as Meriden, Connecticut. Then Weston, with some other member of the firm, would take a train to the same point and await the arrival of the machines. Upon receipt, they were placed in temporary storage, and Weston and his companion would start out to sell them.

The sales procedure consisted of selecting a likely customer and descending upon him with a machine loaded on a truck. While the truck waited at the door, the partners would enter the plating establishment and high-pressure the management into accepting the loan of the machine, on the ground that if it did not improve their work and save money within sixty days, they would come and take it away again. Needless to say, the salesmen had such confidence in their product that they knew few platers, after having once tried the machine, would ever be willing to relinquish it.

Perhaps part of this confidence was an early form of the great American art of breaking down sales resistance, all too familiar today. Edward Weston was naturally a confident young man, but part of this confidence, at least, was pure brashness.. According to today's idiom, he had "nothing to lose." The speaker goes on:

Having accomplished such a sale, the two partners would have the machine taken from the truck and set up in the plating room. Here they would instruct the plater in its use, and needless to say, Weston's knowledge of plating baths and plating methods usually enabled him to suggest some improvement which reflected to the credit of the plater.

This method was so successful that I know of only one instance in which a failure was scored. In this case the machine was thrown out after the trial period, much to the astonishment of the two salesmen. Their confidence was restored, however, after they made a more careful investigation of the situation and discovered that the owner of the establishment was the nephew of a competitor manufacturing a plating machine in the same town. So much for making a sales investigation after the facts, instead of before. Suffice to say that by this and other sales methods, over one thousand plating machines were sold in a relatively short time.

Although the record does not say so, the competing machine was in all probability made by the Wallace-Farmer Company, of Bridgeport. Professor Farmer, as has been mentioned, had preceded Weston by a number of years in marketing a dynamo, with the help of Wallace, who ran a small machine shop. In spite of local popularity, Farmer's dynamo was so poorly designed that Wallace gave up making it altogether in 1878. The most cogent reason for Weston's growing success in Connecticut, and elsewhere, too, was that no other inventor had been able to work out a design nearly so compact or simple or inexpensive to build and run. Weston machines at this early period were marketed at $125 for the smallest size and $500 for the largest. The latter, and a huge electric generator for those days, was twenty inches in diameter and was suitable for the largest plating works. These were the only dynamos in America that bore any close resemblance to modern machines, the reason being that Weston's mind naturally worked toward engineering designs in which efficiency rather than convention was the guiding star. His competitors did not.

How Edward Weston spent his days traveling all over the north-eastern United States on sales expeditions, and yet had time to continue his laboratory work, it is difficult to see. Probably he did these two things by bursts, which was characteristic of him, driving one activity to its farthest limit for the time being, then switching to the other and giving it the same treatment. It is a fact, however, that he kept his place in the forefront of the rapidly accelerating art by continuing to make fundamental discoveries.

Always restless and unsatisfied with the area of experiment he happened to be covering at the moment, Weston was of course aware of the tremendous possibilities of electric power for turning the wheels of industry. He could see that important gains could be made in flexibility and convenience if electric motors could be substituted for mechanical drive. At that time, the steam engine was the only source of mechanical power and had been developed to a reasonably high state of perfection. Every factory that required lathes or other machine tools had its boiler plant and engine, and its ceilings were filled with a vast network of master shafts, counter-shafts, pulleys, idlers, and reversing mechanisms. Thousands of feet of leather belting reached down, connecting every machine separately with the source of primary power. Dripping oil from the overhead pillow blocks, noise, dirt, and considerable hazard were the annoyances to be put up with. The engineer at the end of the shop "rode" the throttle of his engine continually, in a vain endeavor to keep the speed of the shafting steady in spite of the constantly changing load, as one machine after another came into play or was stopped, meanwhile trying to keep the steam pressure on his boiler abreast of the varying power demand. It was not a very satisfactory system, but like everything else that is an influence in human affairs, it was accepted as inevitable, and men swore by it and regarded it as permanent. Edward Weston, however, looked ahead to better things. Although he knew that shop owners would doggedly oppose any improvement, no matter how valuable it might be, he faced the fight with energy and with joy. What he saw in the future was a steam engine running a dynamo which distributed power to electric motors on every machine. It was a wonderful concept. But it is an accurate commentary on the snail's pace of mechanical progress that even today many hundreds of shops still use overhead shafting and belts rather than machines individually driven by their own motors. It has taken seventy-five years even to approximate the realization of this early dream.

At the first moment that Weston had time to spare, he designed and built a dynamo to be run as a motor, and installed it in his own shop for driving some of his lathes and planers. As he had expected, it did the job handsomely, and he made it a permanent part of his equipment. This motor is credited with being the first regularly used in any factory in America. It proved Weston's theory that mechanical energy could be "transformed" and transmitted over wires, then changed back again into rotational power, with more flexibility and at little more expense than the clumsy system of solid shafting and flapping belts between engine and work.

The owners of a nearby textile mill—the Clark Thread Works—were so impressed with Weston's electric motor that they asked him to build and install one in their plant for operating special machines. The installation is believed to have been the first commercial electric power drive in this country. But it was not very successful, for the inventor immediately ran into acute technical difficulties, whose solution was to take a great many years. These were difficulties of speed regulation and control, of starting the motor under load without burning it out, and of preventing serious injury to the machine when a sudden overload developed in the tools it was driving. These problems kept him constantly busy inventing ingenious cutouts, automatic switches, governors, and voltage regulators, which he turned out at a furious rate and tried out in his own shop. If they worked well enough, he offered them to his customers. He was so busy with so many other things, however, that he did not get around to patenting these devices till 1882. Then, with Edison and many other brilliant men in competition with him, he brought out a system of "electric power transmission," complete with control mechanisms, and received patents on every element of it.

## 6

But Weston's principal interest remained with the improvement of his dynamo. In dealing with so complex a mind as his, it is impossible to keep his inventions in their proper·sequence; thus, some of the work on efficiency already mentioned was not done until the plating machine had become a commercial success. In fact, the greatest impetus toward dynamo improvement came late in 1877 and in '78, when the technical world was beginning to awake to electric power in general. The years from 1877 on, therefore, showed the greatest yield of patents.

There was no great difficulty in competing with the efficiency of the few dynamos then on the market. No one of them could show better than 40 per cent over-all efficiency, and figures ranging from 15 to 30 per cent were much more common. The trouble was almost wholly electrical—losses in the form of heat within the machine itself. It was this problem of heating which he now tackled with the greatest energy. As early as 1877 he had arrived at a machine which had the extraordinary *electrical* efficiency of 97 per cent, while the over-all commercial figure (electrical and mechanical efficiencies combined) had been pushed close to 90 per cent. In his early models he was able to obtain this excellent performance only by using very expensive construction. His problem now was to simplify and improve basic designs so that these high theoretical efficiencies could be realized in commercial machines.

Most of the increased efficiency was obtained by careful proportioning of the iron and copper in the dynamo, eliminating as far as possible any metal which was not "working." It was still believed, by all experimenters including Weston, that dynamo armatures should be very long for their diameter, so that the wires actually cutting magnetic flux would be long in proportion to the "end turns," which did not cut across the field. It remained for young Professor Elihu Thomson of Philadelphia to discover, some years later, that armature conductors must be treated as coils, or turns, rather than straight bars and hence that all parts of such coils helped to produce the generated voltage. This principle soon reduced the unnecessary length along the axis and permitted narrow machines of much larger diameter, with the end turns of the windings often longer than the parts parallel to the shaft. Thus, much slower rotating speeds were required for a given rapidity of cutting the field flux. Long cylindrical armatures would not come back until the very high speeds of steam turbine drive made it imperative to cut down the diameter of the rotating part.

Everyone in the seventies, therefore, was struggling with the long armature and the excessive amounts of steel and copper inherent in its faulty proportions. Many ingenious arrangements were advanced to overcome the awkward shape. Weston's were among the most logical. He understood that he must push the loading on iron and copper to the limit, making every part as small as possible for a given power output. The result was a beautiful compactness and—serious heating.

One of Weston's early armature designs was a simple disk of cast iron, with two coils around it at right angles to each other. This was placed inside a 12-inch field frame taken from a standard plating dynamo. An interesting sidelight was that the winding was done by William L. Stevens, the son of the head of the parent firm. Young Stevens was learning to be a toolmaker; his father thought so well of Weston that he wished to have his son take his apprenticeship with him. Will worked for the inventor more than sixty years.

The disk-armature dynamo was more of a novelty than a commercial success. It worked well enough but did not have sufficient output to be adopted as a commercial type. Weston only tried it to prove that he could keep such an armature cool by natural air circulation. Though it did run cool enough, it was obviously not the solution to the heating difficulty. Stevens connected it up to the electric supply lines in the shop and used it as a motor to run his coil-winding machine. He found it a great improvement over winding the coils in a foot lathe, as he had been doing previously.

The single-disk arrangement, however, was the forerunner of the long multiple-disk armature already described, and this was for some time a component of the commercial machines. But the multiple disks with their paper insulating spacers ran too hot, even though Weston bored holes through them to let in the air.

One rather interesting excursion into unusual arrangements of electrical components Weston covered in a patent issued to him in 1878. Here his dynamo had been turned inside out, with a two-pole field magnet mounted on the shaft of the machine, and a cylindrical frame with eight coils wound inside it, doing duty as the armature. Apparently no such machine was ever built for sale, although it had some obvious advantages in the ease of dissipating heat through the outside shell. It was an interesting forerunner of the turbine-driven alternators of today, which use stationary armatures and rotating fields.

Another point of Weston's attack upon armature heating was the separation of the coils from the metal by winding them in transverse slots parallel to the shaft. This was considerably more efficient than the single-disk armature. But, being of solid steel it canceled out the advantages of easy cooling by reintroducing the large eddy-current losses that all were struggling to avoid. A further reason against it was that it contained too many infringements. Everybody else was trying slotted armatures too. It was becoming a clever game indeed to produce a machine that would not instantly bring down an avalanche of lawsuits.

Still another forerunner of modern electrical machinery invented and patented by the young Englishman was a hollow-drum armature supported by end bells connected to short sections of shaft. The coils were wound around this lengthwise and separated by steel bars to improve the magnetic paths. These bars were provided with rows of holes passing inward to the hollow interior. As the armature rotated, the air inside the drum was picked up by centrifugal action and thrown out through the holes, creating a strong circulation. Access for cool air was provided through holes in the end bells. This patent, though applied for in February of 1878, was not granted till the end of 1880. It had taken the Patent Office examiners more than two years to make up their minds that Weston had not infringed any prior claims. The days of applying for protection one month and getting it the next were over. Never again would the United States Patent Office catch up with the inventors who were flooding it with claims in ever-increasing volume.

Just how serious and unavoidable the heating problem was in the late seventies is shown by an elaborate construction which Weston tried out next—using the rather obvious but clumsy scheme of cooling by means of circulating water. After some little work on the idea he decided that it was unnecessary for the small machines the company was then making. But a little later (in the summer of 1877, now) Weston went to Boston to find out why it was impossible to sell his plating dynamos there. He learned quickly enough that two competing makes had saturated the market: the Wallace-Farmer dynamo and one manufactured by a man named William Hochhausen. The latter was particularly exasperating to Weston because he felt that the man was an out-and-out infringer. Mr. Hochhausen was equally annoyed and within a year the two were in court, fighting tooth and nail. It had developed that Hochhausen was installing water-cooled dynamos in plating plants. He was suing Weston for infringement of his patent for the cooling system.

In his testimony, Weston put his finger on the secret of the whole thing:

I have been building machines for plating and other purposes since the latter part of 1872 or the early part of 1873, and did build and sell machines in 1874, almost identical with those now sold by Mr. Hochhausen, and since Mr. Hochhausen began building machines for plating purposes in 1876, I have been very much annoyed by finding that as soon as I had a new device on the machine Mr. Hochhausen followed suit; and I think that I have traced channels through which information given by me has been carried to him; particularly in regard to what is known as the automatic switch. . . .

—as well as various circuit arrangements and the idea of water-cooling the armature. Weston told the court that he had begun water-cooling armatures in 1874, simply by dousing them with a hose. Naturally, this was only for a test, but it had worked well enough to implant the idea in the inventor's head for future use if necessary. When, in 1877, much larger machines came in demand, notably to gain a fair share of the Boston trade, Weston included water cooling.

He had found, in the latter part of that year, that his large machines could not be sold without some form of cooling. He chose water as a medium, because it was so much more efficient than air circulated by natural draft. He made the application reluctantly, because he knew that the real way to get rid of the heat was through a design that would not permit it to be generated in the first place.

However, large machines were in demand, and this was a fairly satisfactory stopgap. He accomplished it by substituting solid end bells for the usual spiders that held the journals of the machine, then pumping water in at one end of the dynamo and out at the other, being careful to keep the outflow pipe well below the journal so that there would be no leakage. It was not a scientifically sound scheme, owing to the danger of impairing the electrical insulation on the armature, and also because of rust. But it saw him through a tough period of competition.

Weston never patented the idea, but Hochhausen did, having "borrowed" it, along with other things, from his Newark competitor.

Hochhausen lost the suit, it being proved that he had placed an accomplice in Weston's shop, who transmitted to him drawings and specifications of anything that looked promising. The case had its slightly amusing side, for the invention which caused his downfall was only a temporary measure and had no future at all.

Weston understood the basic requirements of high efficiency perfectly, but in that early day he could not fully meet them. The dynamo patents which he applied for in '77 and '78 all included some form of cooling. But air, not water, was the medium. In some of them he used a mechanical blower, in others an openwork construction of the armature. This latter, combined with the multiple-disk arrangement of the armature core, gave greatly improved efficiency by cutting down the eddy-current losses. An extension of this principle—and this again was a pioneer advance clearly made by Weston—was the use of laminated *field* iron also. He had discovered that there were fluctuations in the field magnetism, resulting from the reaction of the armature upon it, and that this set up eddy currents and produced heat in the field structure.

The final solution of the heating problem was the use of exceedingly thin laminations of special *silicon* steel, which had very high magnetic permeability. At the time Weston was building dynamos this steel had not been developed, nor had the rolling mills learned how to produce uniform sheets as thin as ten thousandths of an inch.

Actually, by the middle of the Second World War, silicon steel was produced in sheets as thin as one-and-one-half thousandths of an inch. When the new radar art began, such thin material was needed for the tiny transformers used on air-borne radar sets. The rolling mills said it could not be made. But it was made, after engineers had sat up many a night devising new machinery to do it. In Weston's time, however, inventors made use of what materials they had, and circumvented their difficulties with odd mechanical arrangements. Weston was one of the first men in the electrical industry to insist that materials must be "tailored" to suit the needs of the new art.

7

In the summer of 1878 the city of Paris undertook to put on a world-girdling Mechanical Exposition, to demonstrate every phase of the art. Inventors in both hemispheres sent the best examples of their work. Edison was represented; so were twenty-five-year-old Professor Thomson, the venerable Professor Farmer, and a young man named Charles Francis Brush. Gramme and Siemens contributed the best that Europe could produce in dynamos and electric motors. Ayrton of England exhibited a crude ammeter and voltmeter. And Weston sent his latest dynamo.

But by all odds the most spectacular display in Paris that summer was a long row of electric arc lamps, known as the "Jablochkoff Candles," installed and operated by a youthful Russian engineer, Paul Jablochkoff. In *Beloved Scientist* I have described this spectacular exhibit in some detail: "The great showpiece of the Exposition was a fine display of electric arc lights running the whole length of L'Avenue de l'Opéra and around the Place de l'Opéra as well, a full half mile of flooding brilliance. Such an illumination had never been attempted anywhere in the world. The size and wonderment of the crowds seemed to show that electric lighting had been accepted as the only kind worth having. It had remained for the French to show the world the way."

But the display was really nothing but a stunt, and a hugely expensive one, at that. "The ornate rows of Jablochkoff Candles along the Avenue were lighted by a battery of Gramme dynamos nearby, especially built for the occasion. The current they delivered was of the alternating variety, without commutators, and their efficiency was exceedingly low. The apparatus necessary to keep the arcs lighted up was complicated and expensive and had to be constantly repaired. It was in no sense a commercial installation."

It was, in fact, principally an advertising trick invented by the clever Gramme, who never missed a chance to show his wares in public. However, it lighted the world with the brilliance of an explosion. Thomson, who was there in person, rushed home to begin work upon an arc-lighting system of his own.

Edward Weston, true to his determination never to set foot in Europe again, had remained in America. But, immersed as he was in the improvement of the dynamo, he was catching the electric-lighting fever too.

His dynamo had won a great honor in Paris, being awarded a bronze medal. He had sent it there not merely as an example of his advances in the electroplating art but as a contender for a position in the wider field of electric power. It had won distinction in competition with the two greatest names in dynamo history: Siemens and Gramme.

At home in America the three years 1877 to 1880 marked the period of almost violent birth of the electric-lighting art. Suddenly it had become possible to generate electric current in sufficient quantity and cheaply enough to produce great illumination. The brilliant arc which Sir Humphry Davy had struck in 1808 between rods of carbon by using two thousand voltaic cells, worked just as well when supplied by a dynamo one could hold in his hand. Hardly waiting to discover whether the electric arc was commercially feasible, every experimenter who could scrape the money together rushed into a machine shop and developed a system of his own. This included a dynamo, an arrangement of wires, and a lamp structure to hold the carbons together, then draw them apart to strike the arc.

At first there were not many who cared to risk their time and money for this wild venture. Electric lighting was a consumer's invention. It would be used directly by and for the public. And citizens of that day were not quite so receptive to technical innovations as we are now. Bell had just earned the reputation of being a crazy man, not by promising but actually by *proving* that he could talk over electric wires. Edison was still shut up tightly in his laboratory, working on the "subdivision of the electric light" by incandescent filaments. In fact, as this absurd controversy on subdivision raged, even scientists were apt to laugh at each other's discoveries. Many did laugh at Edison. It was actually believed by no lesser men than Sir William Preece, Britain's great electrical authority, that only one lamp could be operated by any one electric current. You could not divide the light up into several luminous points independent of each other. Professor Joseph Tyndall remarked humorously that he would rather have Edison struggle with the problem than do it himself.

The truth of it was, simply, that the carbon arc had very definite characteristics as to voltage and current and could be made to burn properly only at one set of values and with one level of brilliance. Hence, it appeared to be indivisible. But there was nothing to prevent stringing a number of lights along a single circuit, in *series,* using the same current to operate them all, and supplying enough voltage to care for the sum total of the drops across all the arcs. This the inventors very quickly began to do. Edison soon showed that incandescents could burn in multiple as well as in series, and the controversy passed into history. The arc lamp, however, grew up as a series-connected device, because the voltage drop across it was too low to permit economical electric distribution in a multiple circuit. Thus the subdivision objectors prevailed, in a manner of speaking. Even today most street arcs are operated on this series principle.

Controversy or not, there were few enough contenders in 1878 to give an arc-lamp inventor serious trouble. In fact, there were only six starters in the race who were important: Farmer, Thomson, Brush, Weston, and two smaller men: Hochhausen and Palmer. Only half of these survived. Farmer was old and tired. His great monuments were completed: the fire alarm telegraph system and certain mechanisms in the naval torpedo. He ceased to be a contender when, in 1877, the Franklin Institute tested his dynamo against two others and found that it showed an over-all efficiency of only 14 per cent, against 38 for its poorest competitor. Palmer, a Boston engineer, simply did not have the backing and the inventive ability to keep up with the others. Hochhausen, as we have seen, worked in the shadow of dishonesty and was presently eliminated. That left only Elihu Thomson, Charles Brush, and Edward Weston. These three were, indeed, the true pioneers in electric arc lighting.

Elihu Thomson was a professor of chemistry in Philadelphia in the late seventies and was just making a start in the electrical field. His first important contribution was the closed-core alternating-current transformer, and his thinking at this stage was involved mainly with electrical distribution by the a-c system. He did not design a direct-current dynamo till 1879—seven years after Weston had begun his own experiments. And though his first commercial venture, the Thomson-Houston Company, did do its principal business in arc lighting, this did not come until 1880. Then he became a major contender and the nucleus around which a major unit of the electrical industry was built.

Charles Francis Brush, however, was from the start the successful contender for top honors in electric lighting, and deserves the principal credit for developing a practical arc system. Brush began as an Ohio farm boy who was fascinated with electricity. But the demands of earning a living forced him to become a chemist. He did not have time or money to build a dynamo till 1876, when he was twenty-seven years old. Like Weston at an earlier age, he was employed by an electrical concern, the Telegraph Supply Company, and had some access to manufacturing machinery. Unlike him, Brush had a very difficult job persuading his employers to take his dynamo seriously. However, late in 1876 he induced the company to start manufacture in a small way, and from that moment became the unquestioned leader in arc lighting.

Brush had the advantage of complete devotion to a single idea: a lighting system composed of a dynamo, wires, and arc lamps. He never did anything else. Consequently, his progress was rapid and his ideas sound. By 1879 he was manufacturing equipment for burning as many as forty arc lamps in one circuit. At Christmas in the previous year he had installed twenty lights in John Wanamaker's Philadelphia store and had begun lighting the streets of Boston. He had even illuminated Niagara Falls by a dynamo driven by a hydraulic turbine. The final goal was reached when Brush opened the world's first electric generating station in San Francisco

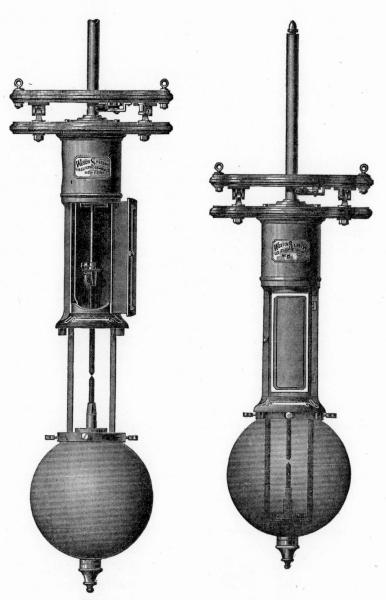

The Weston arc lamp, opened and closed.

—a public utility offering to sell the most intangible yet the most valuable product on earth: electric power.

## 8

Edward Weston's interest in electric lighting reached back considerably beyond Brush's or Thomson's. He had installed his first arc lamp in his own shop on Centre Street in 1874, when he had first constructed a successful plating dynamo. Lighting by electricity continued to intrigue him; in each subsequent shop he installed at least one, to be run from the plating machine mains. However, he made no attempt to develop a commercial lamp until 1877, when the Weston Dynamo Company was formed. From that time on, he was in the thick of the fight.

The birth of commercial arc lighting in 1877–78 found Weston's dynamo in possession of four distinct advantages. It was effectively air-cooled; its laminated-iron magnetic circuit made it the most efficient machine in existence. It had a commutator with spirally laid copper segments, so that there was no serious sparking under load as the brushes passed from one segment to the next. And, lastly, the brushes were adjustable, either by hand or by electromagnets, so that the voltage could be regulated and held nearly constant at different loads.

These features of advanced design gave Weston's dynamo a flexibility and economy no other had—advantages sufficient to offset the more concentrated work Brush had done and to start the two men more or less evenly in the exciting race for light.

Being a chemist it was natural also that Weston should have interested himself in arc-light carbons. He had never forgotten his boyhood experience at the coking ovens, hacking out chunks of carbon for his wet batteries. He felt that he knew this interesting element pretty well. About 1874 he began experimenting with the manufacture of carbon rods, fully aware that if an arc lamp was to burn well it must have material of great uniformity, both in size and chemical composition. Suitable carbons were not made in America; the only ones obtainable came from France and cost $1.20 a dozen. They were a long way from meeting his requirements. His good business instinct told him that as soon as electric lighting became popular there would be an enormous demand for carbon electrodes. He made up his mind to learn how to make them himself.

It was at about the time that he was perfecting his compressed nickel anode that he became interested in arc-lighting carbons. The anode was made of a mixture of powdered nickel and carbon, compacted under pressure. Weston employed the same general scheme to make his earliest lamp rods, using carbon dust and a tar and asphalt binder. The black paste was packed tightly into round moulds by hand, then baked in an oven. The result was a fairly uniform stick of reasonably good strength.

During his first two years in Newark, Weston experimented steadily with arc lights supplied by a plating dynamo, and established the fundamentals of satisfactory operation. Although he had no knowledge of the true electronic action in the arc, he determined, pretty closely, the values of voltage and current that were necessary. An arc would operate over quite a wide range of current values— the more current, the fatter and brighter the flame. He chose an arbitrary figure of 20 amperes as the best, and based all his designs on that.

He had not been experimenting long when he observed that the normal carbon arc gave a very blue light, which was garish and unpleasant. Women who saw it complained that it made them "look dead." Weston realized that this objection would be a very great deterrent to public acceptance, and made up his mind to do something about it. The cure at first seemed to be to shorten and fatten the arc, which increased the temperature and made the light somewhat whiter. However, this remedy was only partial, and there were serious difficulties from heat and from the instability of the arc. The actual distance between carbons was only one thirty-second of an inch—so little that much of the light was lost within the flame itself.

He now came upon an idea that proved to be a basic discovery. It occurred to him to introduce a metal or metal salts into the arc, changing its color to anything desired by properly choosing the material. As a start, he used lime glass. The calcium oxide content burned with a reddish flame, thus reducing the blue glare to a better color.

It was still very early in the electric-lighting timetable when Weston patented this invention on November 26, 1878. And though the device described is exceedingly crude, the claim is worth quoting from, since it was one of the great milestones of the lighting art:

My improvements are of twofold character [he says in his patent No. 210,380]. They relate, first, to devices for introducing into the electric arc a conducting vapor, which, by lessening the resistance between the points of the electrodes, affords an effectual means of retaining the arc in a prescribed path between the electrodes and by its combustion increases the illuminating power of the arc . . . my invention consists in the application to, and consequent combination with, one or each of the electrodes of an electric lamp, candle or torch, but preferably with the positive electrode only, of a cylinder or stick of any material, which, although not placed between the electrodes, is capable of being slowly volatilized by the heat of the electric arc, and which, when volatilized, affords a vapor of better conductivity than the carbon particles, which vapor, by its combustion affects the illuminating qualities of the arc, and by its passage to the negative electrode, fixes and defines the path in which the arc is maintained.

The drawings accompanying the patent showed a pair of carbon rods mounted vertically on a baseboard, one of them being hinged. The rod of lime glass (or other material) stood close alongside the fixed carbon. A second feature of the invention, also basic, was an electromagnet, placed in the lamp circuit, which pulled the movable carbon away from its companion when current was turned on, and thus drew the arc automatically.

What Weston had there was the invention of the "flaming arc," although it was not called that for twenty years. The principal was reinvented after the expiration of this patent and applied universally to making arc lights more pleasing, and more efficient. During the decade of the nineties, flaming arcs were used with many metals to give brilliant color effects, especially outside stores and on theatre marquees. But Weston's name had been forgotten in connection with them. In these later types of carbons the metallic substance was placed inside the carbon as a core. This, also, was Weston's idea.

The aesthetic value of better color was by no means Weston's only reason for inventing the metallic arc. Even more important was the improvement of the efficiency. An arc drawn between two carbon sticks was very unstable and traveled round continually, which made it flicker and give unsteady light. As Weston claimed in his patent, the metal stabilized the arc. When he adopted the cored type of carbons he found that they definitely centered the arc; flickering ceased.

The probable reason why his cored metallic carbons did not find favor at once was that they gave off so much heat that they could not be enclosed in glass. No glass blower in those early days could make a globe that would not melt under the intense heat. When the invention was finally adopted, new types of refractory glass had been found that could stand the strain without blackening or melting away.

Although Weston's work with the arc lamp was fundamental and ingenious and led to highly successful commercial results, it was not his most outstanding contributon to electrical science. Nevertheless, he was able to meet the competition of Brush and Thomson and the growing number of others who soon entered the field. One difficulty he had was that he had adopted too high a current value for operating his lamps. All of the early experimenters were in the dark as to exact theory, and the choice of operating values was a matter of inspired guesswork. By good fortune Brush had hit upon a current value of about eleven amperes, which proved to be the ideal figure. Thomson fixed upon ten; some others adopted as little as four-and-a-half amperes, which was far too small. Weston himself chose twenty.

Long afterward, when the science of electronics at last identified the conditions within an electric arc, it was found that nearly all the voltage is consumed at the surface of the negative electrode and hence is virtually constant for all carbon lamps. The flow of electrons making up the current proceeds from negative to positive carbon, the voltage being used up in helping the electrons to escape *through the surface layer* of the carbon. Once free, the tiny particles move swiftly across the gap, requiring very little voltage drop to propel them.

Now, if too small a current is permitted to flow, the arc will be quite long, but it will be thin and its light will be poor. On the other hand, if too large a current is used, the voltage of electron escape becomes so large a portion of the total that very little is left for the gap itself, and the arc becomes extremely short. This gives a fat white flame, which on first appearance seems to be highly desirable. But it is found that light is given off only by the incandescent carbon tips and by the *surface* of the arc, so that much of it is masked in the interior of the flame and serves no useful purpose. Hence the large added power necessary to produce a heavy-current arc is not answered by a corresponding increase in illumination, and an inefficient light source results.

Brush had hit upon the perfect combination of arc length and fatness to give the most lumens of light per watt of power. Weston, trying to beat him commercially, made the mistake of crowding too much current through his system, thus reducing its efficiency. But he never admitted it. A dogged man who had complete faith in himself, he stuck to his powerful lamps, believing that brute force was the criterion. He had long since abandoned the arc lighting business when the true state of affairs was disclosed by more complete theory.

However, it must be understood that these differences were slight and that in the pioneer days anything that gave electric light at all was bound to sell. Early customers were so intrigued by the novelty of brilliant lighting that they did not count efficiency as very important. Weston, while perhaps behind his competitors in that regard, unquestionably had the best dynamo and a very good control system. So long as his lamps worked, they were bound to find many customers.

9

In the course of his early work on carbons, Edward Weston chalked up another pioneer discovery: the electric arc furnace for the industrial melting of metals. This he did as far back as 1875. He used this method for melting platinum and iridium, two of the most refractory elements common in electrical usage. But he did not patent the idea. Several years later, Siemens did, in Germany, and hence received the credit of being the father of this important branch of metallurgical engineering.

Weston, however, did get the credit for an even more important improvement, when he devised a method of coating the ends of arc-lamp carbons with copper in order to make better electrical contact with the clamps holding them in the lamp. This was a logical procedure for him as a plating expert. As early as 1873 he had immersed rods of carbon in a jar filled with copper sulphate solution and electroplated them with a fine layer of the metal, for the making of positive battery plates. When the arc-lamp industry began to look up, some years later, he revived the idea and standardized upon it, this time using large vats of the sulphate solution, and a dynamo to do the plating. The earliest commercial carbons he plated over their entire length, in order to improve conductivity. Later, only the butts of the carbon rods were plated.

In March of 1877, Weston appeared before the Newark Scientific Association and gave a lecture on dynamos and electric lighting. Young Bill Stevens acted as his assistant. They had with them an electric "hand-lamp"—two carbons mounted vertically on a small wooden base. This lamp used coppered carbons. But the principal thing Weston wanted to show was the safety of the device. The voltage was so low that there was no danger whatever of receiving a shock. We know pretty well now what voltages are dangerous. But in those days the word electricity, most familiar as lightning or as sparks from Wimshurst machines in school laboratories, caused consternation and fear. Any electric current was thought deadly. In proving his crude little "candle" safe, Weston was doing a great service to the future of the industry.

It was a service, however, that would have to be done over and over again. The controversy over the relative hazards of Edison's direct-current system and the Westinghouse Company's a-c power was to rage for nearly fifteen years before a sensible understanding of the real danger would be reached.

Charles F. Brush, in these early years, was just as busy as Weston, and, like so many of the pioneers, invented many things that others had also invented. Early in the game he hit upon the same idea of copperplating his carbons and proceeded to standardize on it. The two men were thus marketing practically the same product. For the moment neither of them had time or money to waste in infringement suits, and by letter they agreed to let each other alone, depending on their commercial prowess to encroach upon each other's territory as much as possible. This worked very well while the field was wide open. But when efficiency began to play a large part and customers stopped to consider which system they had better buy in order to get the best return on their investment, the competitors were forced to look to their rights in order to survive.

At last, in 1882, the Brush Company brought suit against Condit, Hanson, and Van Winkle, who were then producing coppered carbons under Weston's patents. The case dragged on for two years, exposing virtually every detail of arc-lighting history in America— and a good deal of unimportant nonsense besides. Eventually, Brush's suit was lost in 1884.

"The bill for the metal-plated carbon patent was dismissed, with costs, upon the complainant's motion," a contemporary electrical journal exulted. Weston had become the unquestioned originator of the copper-coated carbon rod. And with that he was acknowledged to be the founder of the arc-carbon industry in this country.

Long before the dismissal of the suit he had become the largest manufacturer of this product and was energetically selling carbons to friends and competitors alike. Once started, demand soared and the early hand methods of manufacture proved inadequate. Weston was ready with energetic measures to increase production. *Iron Age* described it thus, in July, 1879:

> Mr. Weston now compresses a finely divided mixture of gas-retort carbon and a small quantity of material destined to increase its adhesiveness, by a powerful hydraulic press into the shape of six-inch cylinders. The latter are introduced into a strong cylinder, which can be heated by steam. The material, thus rendered plastic, is forced through a die having a diameter equal to that of the rods required, by means of a hydraulic press. The carbon is obtained in the shape of a long rod which need only be cut up into lengths, which are slowly dried and are then baked at a high temperature in black lead crucibles. The carbon rods thus obtained are dense and hard, and possess a metallic ring. They are given a slight coating of copper in an electroplating bath, and are then ready for use, their length being about twelve inches and their price 72 cents. One pair of twelve-inch carbons will suffice for eight hours' illumination.

These were production-line methods, although the price of a carbon was hardly a mass-production figure yet. It is interesting that the manufacturing method was almost identical with today's art of producing thermoplastic extrusions. If one had substituted a polymerizing resin for the mysterious "material destined to increase adhesiveness," one would have leaped seventy years into the future at one stride.

Which is slow motion indeed when compared to the meteoric rise of the arc-lighting business in the late seventies. Only two years before the date of the quotation just given, Weston had not been able to sell carbons at all. In fact, he had had to give them away for nothing, in order to induce people to burn his strange new lamps.

## 10

Probably the earliest public exhibit of the arc lamp in America was at the Philadelphia Centennial in the summer of 1876. A flickering but brilliant point of light would occasionally burst from the high peak of Machinery Hall and startle the crowds milling through the stifling night. Few of the people realized that they were seeing the first beacon of a new era. But this was not the world's first demonstration of "commercial" arc lighting. Ten years earlier, an Englishman named Ladd had tried to interest London in these lamps and had only succeeded in frightening the citizens, who much pre ferred the soft haze spread through their city by the dependable gas lamp. Actually, arc lighting had been giving practical service for three years even at that time, having been installed in a number of French lighthouses with very good effect. A contemporary newspaper account describes the still more spectacular electric installation in St. Catherine's Light on the Isle of Wight:

The original mineral-oil lamp has been lately replaced by what is stated to be the most powerful electric light in the world. . . . The engine house contains three of Roby's compound engines, each of thirty-six horse-power, and two De Meritens magneto-electric machines, each capable of producing a light of 3,000,000 candles. . . . There are three lamps; the carbons are two and a half inches in diameter and six-pointed star-shape in section. . . . On a bright night the lantern is clearly seen at a distance of forty miles, and at the Needles, about twelve miles distant, a newspaper has been distinctly read by this powerful flash.

Yet, fifteen years later, with the technical difficulties largely solved, American inventors were having a real struggle to interest their public in their new product.

All of them realized that the most powerful way to create interest was to arrange a public showing—literally to hit people in the eye with the advantages of the arc lamp. Brush, Weston, Thomson, Farmer—all of them were making brave efforts to startle the public into a familiarity with the new system. Cleveland, Boston, Philadelphia, New York, all had their trick displays in 1878 or soon after.

Some months before Brush succeeded in lighting Wanamaker's store in 1878, Weston persuaded the city fathers of Newark to let him put up an arc at the very center of town. "At the time," said his son, in a speech many years later, "the Newark Fire Department had no electrical fire boxes, so it was necessary to keep a constant visual watch over the city, much as forest rangers still do from their towers in the woods. The Department's watch tower was a cast-iron affair, which I well remember. It was perhaps six or eight stories in height, and located on Washington Street, north of Market, about on the site of one of the Prudential Insurance Company buildings. The tower had a glass enclosure at the top and a large bell hanging about half way up. In the glass enclosure firemen were constantly on watch, and reported to the ground any unusual smoke seen during the daytime, or bright light at night."

It was in full view of this commanding point of vantage that Weston installed his first arc-light display—at the corner of Washington and Market streets.

"It was plainly visible on the tower, so that when the arc light was first turned on, the firemen were duly notified and warned not to turn in an alarm. Perhaps it is just as well that this was done, because not only was the light the most brilliant seen in the city, but it straightway gathered a great crowd of people who were attracted by the unusual and beautiful sight."

It is amusing to imagine a crowd gathering today, say in Times Square, to stare at an arc light. Only a group of aborigines visiting New York would do that. Such is the change in the level of human experience in a few decades!

This demonstration alone would have brought in no more business than if the crowds had indeed been composed of South Sea Islanders. But Weston pursued his display advertising technique with his usual vigor. A little later he "considered it desirable" to install a battery of arc lamps on the roof of his synagogue-factory, to test out their ability to stand all kinds of weather. These were often burned day and night. "Whenever this was done," said his son, "the factory was sure to be visited during the next few days by

Electricity comes to the factory: crude arc lamp and motor of the 1870's.

curious and helpful sea captains, who had observed the light from Newark Bay or New York Harbor, had traced its location, and had come to learn and to suggest the desirability of having such lights in lighthouses."

It was inevitable that such displays should create public interest.

The company began to get "bites." During the summer of 1878 the Newark City Council approached Weston and offered to accept one lamp for installation in Military Park. Weston put one up—a powerful light that equaled 7,000 candles, and it drew vast public attention—and millions of bugs and moths. It was believed to have been the first light ever supplied on contract to a municipality. As he had been forced to do with his early plating dynamos, Weston had to furnish both light and the dynamo to drive it, free on several months' trial. This concession had to be given with every prospective customer. But it usually turned out that the lamps attracted so much attention that they were retained—and purchased—even if people blocked the streets looking at them. They provided the most powerful advertising ever invented.

During 1879 Weston made a successful installation in Boston's Forest Garden—one lamp in front of the dancing pavilion, one inside it, and one under the theater marquee. Shortly he had a similar exhibit at Newark's Union Park also. These didn't work very well, because an overzealous assistant of Weston's had broken some of the wires in an effort to screw them down securely.

That summer five more Weston lights appeared at Fort Lee, an amusement center up the Hudson River. Charles F. Beers, a factory hand, put them in. The owner wanted them for the Fourth of July. "I belonged to a benevolent aid club in this city," Beers testified in one of the lawsuits that came nine years later, "and we were going to parade on the morning of the Fourth. While I was waiting for the procession to come along in front of Weston's factory, so as to join it, Mr. Weston asked me to go to Fort Lee. I did not want to go and told him so, but he seemed to get angry and said I must, so I went. . . ."

Weston was in no mood to lay off his men for the holidays. He never was. Commercial survival, to him, meant absolute loyalty to the job, day and night—for him and everybody who worked for him.

Many a night he never went home at all, but stayed in the laboratory, personally testing new lights that were about to be shipped. "Business" kept him occupied all day, he used to say, and left no time for his own work except at night. His assistants, like Edison's nearby, got no quarter; if some new invention was in process, they were expected to hang on till it was completed. "If Mr. Weston thought of any idea," said one of them, "it would have to be worked out immediately, if it took all night."

There wasn't much time, and Edward Weston knew that better than most. It was this sense of urgency that put him in the lead in this business, as in many another.

There was a peculiar hazard with these arc lights that nobody understood—the danger of serious eye injury from the ultraviolet radiation. It was obvious enough that one should not look directly at the arc, any more than one should stare directly at the sun. And Weston had the good sense to adopt smoked glasses for his experimental work. If he had not done so, he would probably have gone blind early in the game. As it was, his eyesight was seriously impaired quite soon after he began work. "I can remember," his son says, "in later years hearing my mother complain that father almost ruined his eyes during this period, as a result of his frequent observation of the arc lamps. In fact, at one period it became necessary for her to lead him from the factory to his home." At times, indeed, she would have to take him there and fetch him back every day, and he suffered from constant headaches, which doctors were many years in assigning to ultraviolet burns.

Such narrow escapes forecast the terrible tragedies that overtook many an eager experimenter with X rays, toward the end of the century. There were so many critical dangers to electricity that it is a wonder that the pioneers survived at all.

In the midst of the drive to establish an electric-lighting business the inventor's second son was born—Edward Faraday Weston— on October 24, 1878. If his father stayed at home from his work that day, or in any way altered his exacting schedule in honor of the event, it is not on record.

Arc lighting, for the moment, was his breath and his being.

## II

The work progressed steadily.

Late in 1879, fire broke out in the front offices of the synagogue-plant on Washington Street and made such a shambles of the place that it was decided to move to a new plant. With the extraordinary dispatch of those days the entire manufacturing establishment was dismantled and set up again in new quarters *one week* after the fire! The location chosen was on Plane Street, and the factory, huge for those days, covered nearly a block. It was standing conveniently empty and Weston took possession of it without complicated negotiations of any kind.

The plant is still standing and still operating—as the Meter Works of the Westinghouse Electric Corporation.

Very soon after the move Weston and his associates decided to change the firm name to the Weston Electric Light Company. With this move they gave notice that they intended to become a serious contender for first place in the mushrooming electric-light field. Their ambitions were not without foundation. The move seemed to inject an extraordinary new vigor into the company's affairs. As the year 1880 began, orders crowded in. It was necessary to buy vacant land beside and behind the plant, and shortly Weston, just ten years from a penniless youth landing at the Battery, had become the proprietor and moving spirit of the largest electric lamp and dynamo plant in the United States. Business was so good that a New York office was needed to handle it.

It was no surprise to find that the Plane Street plant was lighted from end to end by Weston arc lamps, and that Weston dynamos, running in reverse as motors, were driving some of the machinery.

As 1880 arrived electric lighting was just beginning its meteoric rush to popularity. In the previous October, Thomas Edison had finally discovered how to make an incandescent lamp that would burn for a hundred hours before it failed. His young engineer, Francis Upton, had designed a dynamo, and Edison was well along the road toward inventing his famous three-wire distribution system by which electric lights could be supplied over a considerable area from a "central station." There were at least a dozen contenders in the dynamo field now, and every city in the country was being invaded by excited young men who sought local funds to start up a Brush Electric Light Company, a Weston Electric Light Company, a Wood, a Thomson-Houston or some other public utility. The fellow who got there first, with the most appealing arguments, usually got the business.

Weston was getting there first in a sufficient number of instances. One, which brought considerable public attention, was an installation of arc lamps on a hotel construction job at Rockaway Beach, near Coney Island. Said *Leslie's Weekly* at the time:

> In order that the building and grounds may be finished in time for the summer business, it has been found necessary to employ over 1000 men and 100 teams, work being carried on night and day, which, with the aid of the Weston Electric Light, is perfectly feasible, and much time will be saved thereby.

Weston had fitted the lamps with special reflectors and provided a dynamo to supply them with current.

Another first for Weston arc lights was the constructing of the famous Iron Pier at Coney Island, which was to receive uncounted thousands of New Yorkers sailing down the bay on holidays. Weston long remembered the difficulties of this installation. For driving the arc-light generators he had to use a balky engine that had no governor and could not keep to a steady speed. He often spent the night at the pier, firing the boiler himself in an effort to keep uniform steam pressure and so regulate the speed.

The incandescent lamp was never a serious threat to the arc light, for the former was naturally adapted to the lighting of individual rooms, while the arc could not be tolerated except outdoors or in large halls, where the incandescent was entirely ineffective. But gaslight was an arch antagonist to both and now, in 1880, it was so firmly entrenched that the gas companies, powerful everywhere, could afford to laugh at what they mistook for weak competition. Arc-lamp inventors, however, did not intend to be confined to the small business in showy lighting which the gas companies spurned. They proposed to drive the gentle little fan-shaped flames out of business.

It was a tough problem to compete with gas. What could equal the simplicity of the small, lava-tipped pipe protruding from the wall, kindled in a jiffy with one match, and controlled perfectly by a simple stopcock? The arc was a powerful brute, temperamental, and controlled only at the cost of intricate electromagnetic mechanisms. It could not be sure of public acceptance until it became entirely automatic and completely reliable. It is a great tribute to American inventive genius that, within a year or two, every one of the limitations had been overcome, so that arc lighting was not only as cheap and reliable as gas but many times as good.

"What we were confronted with," Weston said in 1915, "was a really serious mechanical problem—that of getting the regulators to keep all the arcs always the same length when they were [operating] in series, because there must be the same amount of energy on each lamp. Therefore, the resistance of the individual lamp must be almost exactly the same for equal lighting power. That difficulty was overcome in quite a variety of ways by both Brush and myself long before the others were reading about means of subdividing incandescent light."

That was the problem—to operate many lights in series, *at the same time,* and still allow the user to turn one or more on or off at will without upsetting the whole system. A single lamp was no good commercially; everybody wanted a whole string of them, under as perfect control as gas.

The first systems were very crude. Everything had to be done by hand. If a customer bought a dynamo and a set of lamps, somebody had to stand over the machine constantly to manipulate its brushes so that when some lights were turned off the increased voltage would not swamp the others and blow them up. Every inventor immediately had to devise an automatic regulator, either on the dynamo or in the lamp. One reason Elihu Thomson succeeded so well was that he had an electromagnetic regulator that automatically shifted the generator brushes in response to the load. His company maintained its advantage in 1880, when Thomson and his partner, Edwin Houston, invented a *constant current* dynamo in which regulation was built in electrically. No matter how many lights were in circuit, the amperage remained the same; hence the lights could not be oversupplied.

As Weston saw it, the simplest form of regulation was to build the control into the lamp itself, making it self-sustaining and self-eliminating if it went out. In pursuit of this end, he took out no less than thirteen patents on lamp mechanisms in the two years between 1880 and '82.

All arc lamps were similar in basic arrangement: The two carbons faced each other end-to-end, vertically, the lower one being fixed, the upper moving up and down to adjust the gap and maintain the arc. The control mechanism manipulated this upper carbon. From the beginning, inventors had used some sort of electromagnetic clutch which held the carbon rod and automatically dropped it when the material burned short and the arc went out. Weston's clutch was similar to the others. The problem was to feed it down evenly and not drop it suddenly.

In October, 1880, he was discussing with his patent attorney, Chauncey Smith, in Boston, the matter of improvements in clutch mechanisms, when Smith suggested that any kind of a clutch at all would probably be an infringement on others.

"I think you would do well, Weston, to try something entirely different," he said.

Weston went back to Newark and set to work devising a new lamp mechanism. Shortly he had invented a carbon feed which incorporated a chamber containing mercury, with a float to which the upper rod was attached. The scheme worked perfectly well, and a number of test lamps were produced in the shop. But just as the model was ready to go into production, Weston scrutinized it more closely and decided that it was too vulnerable and so abandoned it. It seemed better to him to invent his way around other patented feed mechanisms than to introduce something entirely new.

This decision yielded a long line of ingenious and increasingly intricate arrangements, which he promptly covered by patents. The whole scheme of the thing was to employ the slight voltage rise which occurred when the carbons burned off and the arc gap lengthened, to hitch the upper carbon downward slightly and shorten the gap again. One of Weston's first ideas involved a ratchet wheel connected to the carbon rod through a pulley and cable, and worked by an electromagnet. This was soon followed by a more effective method, using the differential principle—one magnet in series with the arc, the other across it. As the arc lengthened the series magnet weakened and the shunt coil strengthened. The tendency for the two to balance provided a delicate control. But the mechanism was pretty complicated.

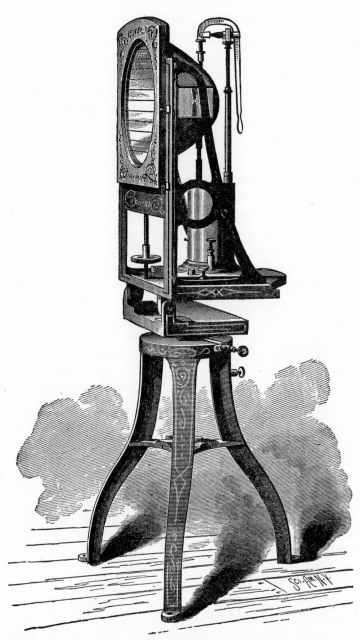

Prototype of the theater spotlight. The carbons were adjusted by hand.

As time went on, the inventions were more and more in the nature of refinements on the same basic principle. At one point [this patent was granted in September, 1882] Weston changed from plain magnets to solenoids, using the motions of two plungers transmitted through a closely designed set of cams and links, to move his carbon downward. This also worked well and required considerably less power to be diverted from the main circuit, since the solenoid is a more efficient means of transforming magnetic energy into mechanical force.

Still another variation was a "derived circuit" magnet, operated by a rise in temperature at the arc. A small box containing a fusible wire was placed close to the arc. If it lengthened too much and heated up, the wire melted, the magnet operated, and the lamp was short-circuited. This was not so much a control mechanism as a safety device. Lamps were now being operated in strings of fifteen or more. If their feed mechanisms stuck and they went out, the full circuit voltage could be impressed across the faulty one, quickly ruining it.

By 1881 practically everybody who made arc lamps had solved the worst difficulties, and Weston was holding a very high place among them.

In this year the city of Paris again held an electrical exposition, and the Weston Electric Light Company made a prominent showing there. But the situation of three years before had changed. Arc lighting was one of the biggest features of the exhibit, and competing systems were legion. Gramme, Siemens, Edison, Brush, Maxim, Lonton, Crompton-Burgin, Gulcher, Jablochkoff, de Meritens, Weston—all were there. Of them all, Hiram Maxim was perhaps the most spectacular. As chief electrician for the United States Electric Lighting Company in New York, his brilliant and fruitful mind was at the moment passing through its electric-lighting phase, before going on to greater things. Weston was destined to be a partner of Maxim's a little later on, and then to wish he had never set eyes on him.

Weston's patents covered almost every item in an arc lamp and served as the basis for an extremely profitable business venture, which was further aided by his virtual control of carbon electrode manufacture. He was in an enviable position indeed. The patents included not only mechanisms, but the original safety fuse, composed, simply, of a strip of metal melting at a very low temperature, mounted upon a block of wood between two terminal posts. This was the forerunner of the ubiquitous little fuse plug which every householder has met with in dark cellars to his sorrow.

But by far his greatest contribution to the art was the high-resistance shunt circuit which he standardized upon for all his lamps. This comprised a magnet coil in series with the lamp, having another coil of German silver wire concentrically wound upon it. When the lamp was first turned on, current flowed in both coils, and the armature piece, drawn toward the poles, lifted the carbon electrode and established the arc. At the same time it interrupted the shunt circuit and removed the German silver winding from operation. The virtue of this was that if the lamp should fail for any reason, the mechanism would introduce into the lighting circuit a resistance equal to the arc when operating properly. Thus, other lamps would not be affected by the failure.

The Paris Exposition of 1881 was really the rising curtain for world-wide electric lighting. Tom Edison was putting the finishing touches to a complete incandescent system, and within a year would open the world's first electric light plant—the famous Pearl Street Station. In the arc-lighting field Brush and Weston were the acknowledged leaders. According to Sir William Preece in England, Weston's system was clearly the best mechanically. Preece had found it wise to retire from his earlier contention that the electric light could not be "subdivided," and was industriously approving of the whole art as rapidly as he could.

12

Here in America the business was rapidly approaching a state of private civil war. A town which had no electric lights would be invaded by various competing teams, and while there was not much actual shooting, there was plenty of vilification, political finagling, and occasional hijacking of supplies and laborers, as one aggressive sales force met another. "Each of the pioneer manufacturing companies," said the *Electrical World,* "was possessed with a religious zeal for converts to its own particular 'system'—which made each promoter deny that any virtue was to be found in the camps of his rivals."

By today's standards such behavior would be considered highly reprehensible among scientific rivals. It was not, then.

Now that the art had become a vigorous industry, and public acceptance had created a dependable and expanding market, the various contenders began to look around them for patent protection. There was not much to be had, for the overworked Patent Office examiners, buried under the deluge of applications, were generously protecting everybody for almost exactly the same thing. In other words, the electric light business had become a chaotic mass of infringements—and infringements of infringements. If any one of the inventors had been able to make good on all his claims, not another person in the United States would have been able to sell a single arc lamp.

Thus the period of the middle eighties was the beginning of the great heyday of litigation. Everybody sued and went to court. Judges and attorneys found themselves inextricably entangled in technical claims so nearly identical that the only hope of unraveling them was to establish some kind of priority by means of detailed examinations into personal histories before specially appointed masters. Court cases of this period dragged on for as much as five years and frquently ended in a draw, with nobody profiting except the lawyers. Clearly, business could not be conducted with all the principal workers arguing for their lives in stuffy courtrooms.

Weston's big case was fought by his agents, Condit, Hanson & Van Winkle, against Brush, beginning in December, 1880. Brush, the complainant, claimed infringement of two of his patents, one covering metal-coated lamp carbons, the other a "completely automatic arc lamp," including a clutch arrangement and many other devices. A brilliant array of legal stars was lined up for each side. Brush called in three college professors and an engineer as expert witnesses; Weston relied mostly on himself and his patent attorney, Edward E. Quimby. The case started off in the Southern District of New York but was later switched to Hartford, Connecticut, occasioning severe hardship to both inventors and their technical associates, who had to waste *approximately four years,* either traveling back and forth to testify or helping others prepare arguments and collect historical data.

Long before the end of the struggle Brush's attorneys petitioned to drop the coated-carbon complaint, acknowledging that the invention had been fully described and used by Weston before Brush patented it. And long before the end of the case, Weston's firm had been absorbed by the United States Electric Lighting Company, and the suit had been shifted to their shoulders.

The suit is mentioned here because it was so typical of the intolerable situation that was hindering the orderly advance of electrical engineering. Obviously, the various contenders would have to learn to live and work together without dissipating their energies in commercial murder. Two attempts were therefore made to relieve matters; a consolidation of the principal patent interests, and the formation of the National Electric Light Association.

The consolidation took the form of a pooling of patents under a holding company called the Gramme Electric Company and was completed in 1882. It obtained control of Weston's arc light and dynamo patents and those of Brush, Fuller, Jablochkoff, and the United States Company; shortly it added some of Edison's as well. The arrangement was no guarantee of industrial peace, however, for it was primarily an agreement among the parties to combine their resources to fight all *outside* infringers. It was effective enough in smoothing the troubled waters of the arc-light interests, but it only set the stage for the grand finale—the titanic battle over the origin of the incandescent lamp. When serious contention arose *within the family,* fratricide followed instantly. But this is a story for a later section.

The National Electric Light Association, which was organized in 1885 and included virtually everybody, was a more beneficent body. Its aim was to prepare the whole lighting field for orderly progress, to bring the many warring interests together *before* they stamped into court, and to cut down the piratical invasions incident to establishing electric systems in new territory. It lived to do a most useful regulatory work in the vast public utility industry.

With consolidation in the air, Weston was naturally on the lookout for a chance to enlarge his horizons. The chance came in 1881, in the midst of a most profitable business year and during the first violences of the struggle with Brush. The United States Electric Lighting Company began buying the Weston Company's stock, and presently had a controlling interest in the enterprise. It was a high compliment to Weston that this group of New York bankers, who controlled the work of the brilliant Hiram Maxim, and of the veteran Professor Farmer, should choose Weston as the one man to improve their own position. But it meant the end of Weston's solo venture in manufacturing.

A few years after the company had absorbed Edward Weston, one of its brochures gave this refreshingly naïve example of the sales talk that was considered necessary in that day:

The United States Electric Lighting Co. was organized in 1878, before any system of electric lighting had been commercially introduced. Believing that the near future would witness the rapid development of electricity as an illuminating agent, its Directors sought the best apparatus to manufacture, and the brightest and most practical electricians. The Company was not formed for speculative purposes, but for the legitimate development of a manufacturing business, and consequently its history is free from imputations of stock gambling and fraud, which are so justly connected with some Electric Light Companies.

Entering the field so early on this comprehensive plan, not being tied down to the inventions of any one man, and with abundant capital, it was able to procure a large number of valuable fundamental patents and the services of several eminent inventors and electricians.

They did not say that the reason they bought out Weston was that they badly needed a dynamo to compete with Brush, Jimmy Wood, and Thomson-Houston; and that Weston was the only man that had it. Yet this was the purpose in making the deal.

The United States Company had been manufacturing in New York. Now, with the purchase of the Weston Electric Light Company, the concern moved its center of gravity to Newark, and took up quarters in Weston's factory at Plane and Orange Streets. There was practically no change in the setup except the enlargement that came from the welcome inflow of new capital. Edward Weston, as always, became the focal point for all engineering and production activities. He was named Consulting Electrician for the company, and took on the duties of Works Manager as well.

This restless and self-assured man had made another great stride forward. He was now fully revealed on the world stage, illuminated in the light of his own inventions.

Brooklyn Bridge blazes with Weston light.

### 13

One of the first important contracts which the company received was the lighting of the new Brooklyn Bridge with two rows of Weston arc lamps on ornamental poles. The Weston dynamo to run them, with all subsidiary equipment, was housed in a small building on the Brooklyn side.

This greatest monument to John A. Roebling, America's most famous builder of suspension bridges, was completed in 1883 and opened with a tremendous celebration on May 24. President Chester Arthur and Governor Grover Cleveland of New York drove across the bridge at the head of a huge parade which included almost every notable of the day. An entire afternoon was expended in speeches, bandplaying, and inspection tours of the marvels of the new structure, while streets and rooftops were packed with a mammoth crowd estimated in the millions. But the evening celebration dwarfed what had come before.

"At eight o'clock," says D. B. Steinman, in his biography of Roebling, "the first fuse was touched off, releasing fifty giant rockets, and a few seconds later the two cities lay under a sparkling shower of gold, blue, red, and emerald fire. From both shores burst fountains and jets and tremendous geysers of varicolored flames and living cascades of brilliance eclipsing the stars.

"Countless thousands witnessed the unforgettable spectacle. They saw the span flooded with the miracle light of eighty powerful *electric* lamps strung along the arching roadway! And above the Bridge, they beheld the flight of numberless bombs and rockets, together with great showers of gold and silver rain, and Niagaras of fiery sparks and floating stars."

If Weston himself was there, we have no record of it. He made no speeches; his lights celebrated his fame instead. The chances are that he was in his shirt sleeves in the power house beneath the Brooklyn tower, watching like a hawk as his men closed switch after switch and the sturdy little dynamo picked up its load. This was the most spectacular installation of arc lamps he ever made, and he was proud of it.

So proud, that his son Edward can still remember a great day when he was no more than five or six, when his mother led him by the hand along South Street, to see the great soaring span of the bridge, and the lights which his father had installed "in the sky."

### 14

If Edward Weston had invited trouble and hard work as a contender in the arc-lighting race, he now found himself in a field in which trouble was utterly certain. With the independence of his new consulting position, and the larger funds available for laboratory experiment, he was able for the first time to take up long-deferred work on incandescent lighting. Here was perhaps the greatest single advance in human well-being ever devised by man. And the inventors of it were bitterly at each other's throats.

Throughout the United States, Thomas A. Edison is known as

the man who invented the incandescent lamp. In the public mind it is as though everyone in America had stood perfectly still, breathlessly waiting for Mr. Edison to accomplish the impossible. This is as wide of the fact as are most popular notions about science. It is true that Edison's brilliant ability to cut through to the fundamentals of a problem and devise a solution resulted in the first commercially practical electric light. In addition, his natural sense of timing and his talent for showmanship helped him to publicize his invention and procure world-wide acceptance for it. But, so far as history is concerned, he was not the sole inventor of electric incandescence. In fact, the first Edison lamp came some 59 years after the Frenchman, De La Rue, had produced an electric "glow" by heating a coil of platinum wire in a glass tube.

Many investigators followed De La Rue, all of them trying to obtain useful light from the heating of a wire by electric current. For many decades they failed, because all of them believed that a metal conductor must be used. No metal then known had a high enough resistance to make it light up with any reasonable current. Platinum was the best, but it was far too expensive.

By Edison's time the basic elements that would make a successful incandescent lamp had been separately suggested: a glowing element of high-resistance carbon rather than metal, and a sealed glass container exhausted of air to prevent oxidation and burning of the conductor. It was Thomas Edison's genius for simplification that showed the world how to put these things together into a practical whole. He reduced the conductor to a fine thread, or "filament," and raised it to white heat by using a high voltage and little current. He formed the thread into a loop and mounted it upon two metal lead-in wires, which he sealed into the base of a glass globe, the base acting as a support. Finally, he exhausted the air from the globe and sealed it hermetically.

A number of people had tried these things before Edison. But no one had conceived this beautifully simple combination *as a whole.* His basic patent on it had a clear priority, at least in the United States. But it had hardly been granted when several other inventors hurried into the field with patents that covered nearly the same thing, and began making and selling lamps of their own, Weston among them. And in the invention of the homogeneous carbon filament he corrected the one weak point in Edison's system: the short life which made the earliest carbon lamps impractical. But the story of this discovery comes a little later.

Exactly as in the case of arc lighting, the successful incandescent lamp brought on a chaos of litigation. Edison's backers, the most powerful financial interests in the country, adroitly engineered a series of purchases and consolidations, grouping supporting patents into an impenetrable wall of legal protection, and then haled the rest of the patentees into court. The record-breaking case, involving scores of lamp makers here and abroad, ended in a clear victory for Edison. Everyone, everywhere, either had to stop making lamps or obtain a license from Edison's company to continue making them. For a time there was great bitterness over the decision, but now, in the calmer light of retrospect, it is agreed that the courts acted fairly. Edison, and Edison alone, had discovered the workable lamp, whose main feature was the sealed-in wires in an exhausted bulb. Able patent attorneys had covered the invention so thoroughly that any other lamp that would operate at all was an infringement.

By the time the case was decided, Weston's lamp patents had passed to Westinghouse, along with the United States Company, and were casualties along with the rest. The loss of the Weston patents almost ruined Westinghouse—a fact that was demonstrated in 1893, when this company obtained the contract to put up thousands of incandescent lamps at the Chicago World's Fair. The lamps had just been completed when word came that the courts had invalidated their patents. In a terrible scramble to save this large piece of business, company scientists hastily invented the "stopper" lamp—a bulb not sealed at the bottom but closed by a glass stopper with a ground joint. It was an expensive expedient, but it saved the day. Stopper lamps were not practical for sale to the public and disappeared after successfully performing at Chicago. Westinghouse, like everybody else, became a licensee of General Electric under the Edison sealed-bulb patents.

J. W. Starr, an American, obtained the first patent on incandescent lamps in 1845, describing a carbon rod inside a glass tube temporarily exhausted of air by the dropping of a column of mercury. Moses G. Farmer was another early contender, with a bulb containing a platinum wire. Many other attempts followed, mostly without adequate means of removing the oxygen surrounding the heated element. Platinum was used because it oxidized very little, even when incandescent.

These crude lamps actually burned and gave light, though the cost for power was tremendous. It has been estimated that the platinum-filament lamps of the sixties, supplied by Grove batteries, were burned at a cost of about $100 per kilowatt-hour, and with an illuminating efficiency close to zero!

The key to the whole situation was a good vacuum, and this key was provided in 1875 by the German, Sprengel, who invented a mercury pump which exhausted the air from a vessel by trapping small portions of it between slugs of mercury passing down a tube. In theory, this pump could reduce the air pressure to the vapor pressure of the mercury itself. In practice, it gave a vacuum high enough for making satisfactory incandescent lamps. Inventors everywhere rushed into the fight.

Weston's interest in incandescent lighting preceded Edison's by a year or more. In the spring of 1876, while he was still working on his early dynamos in the little attic laboratory of his home on Eighth Avenue in Newark, he found time to make some experiments with lamps of the type Farmer had used as far back as 1857. As he had no means then of producing a good vacuum, the platinum wire lamp was his only hope. He could not afford more than a little fragment of the precious metal, and immediately ran into the problem of fashioning a strip of uniform cross section, so that it would heat up evenly. It was for this purpose that he invented his electric arc furnace, this being the only possible way for him to heat and work platinum. During the experiments Weston also tried iridium, but that was more expensive still. Almost the only good that came out of the trials was the arc furnace itself, which has already been described.

Weston very quickly decided that carbon was the only possible element that would be cheap enough and resistant enough to make an incandescent lamp. Carbon was an old friend, too. It was not difficult to have strips cut from ordinary battery-plate material, and in the spring of 1876 he was doing this with interesting results. For bulbs he was using ordinary chemical flasks, with a pair of wires passing through the cork and connected to the carbon strip.

To prevent combustion of the carbon, Weston introduced a little metallic potassium, which rapidly absorbed most of the oxygen in the flask. But this was not satisfactory, and he tried exhausting the air with a small mechanical pump. This also failed. A third alternative, he found, was to put some phosphorus in the flask and burn it, thus combining the oxygen. That, too, worked badly. However, he actually made a "lamp" in that year of '76 that burned two hours before the carbon strip failed.

All of the incandescent lamp pioneers realized that carbon was the ideal filament material. But instead of adopting pure amorphous carbon as Weston had done they were trying to work with cellulosic material such as paper, wood, and thread, carbonizing it by charring it in an oven. Edison, more thorough than any of them, was making an exhaustive search for a fine homogeneous material, which eventually led his assistants to South America and China in pursuit of a fine-grained bamboo. The problem that blocked them all was the extreme difficulty of obtaining any material that would be uniform when reduced to the very small dimensions of a filament. No matter how carefully Edison and his competitors selected their fibers, the stuff was bound to have weak spots. As soon as the current heated it to incandescence, these spots glowed more brightly than the rest, and presently the filament would burn through. Weston used to amuse himself by pointing out such weak places to his little son. "That lamp," he would say, "will burn out in an hour. . . ." And it would.

### 15

Weston approached the problem as a chemist and technician rather than as an explorer. Arguing that there is no fiber in nature which is exactly uniform, he refused to waste time on carbonized thread and slivers of bamboo. He insisted that the carbon must be amorphous, and the final thread a synthetic one carefully fashioned by forcing it into a mould. Immediately putting this thought into practice, he mixed carbon dust with tar and squeezed the resulting paste into a very small opening between two blocks of metal. The resulting "wire" he baked in an oven to form a hard and apparently uniform conductor. But the uniformity was only apparent. Placed in a circuit inside an evacuated bulb, this filament material quickly showed the same weakness as fibrous carbon. Though he experimented for many months he could not achieve an unvarying cross section in the few inches of length that he needed for a lamp. And the slightest unevenness would quickly show up in a rapid burning out of the filament.

Half a century later a brilliant young engineer attempted to design the steel structure of the great 200-inch telescope so rigidly that its own weight would not distort it and throw the optical system out of line. But the more massive he made it, the greater its weight became, and the distortion remained prohibitive. Then he changed his attack: he decided to *let it distort,* and by making the structure like a pin-connected truss, keep the optical axis a straight line even though the steel work deflected considerably. This brilliant solution has virtually avoided distortional errors in the world's largest telescope.

In 1877 Edward Weston had discovered this same principle—that if you cannot avoid an embarrassing obstacle, adopt it and make it work for you. So now, being unable to prevent weak spots in his carbon filament, he decided to make these spots *repair themselves,* by virtue of the very fact that they glowed more brightly than their neighbors when current was passed through them.

"Weston remembered," said Dr. Baekeland in his Perkin Medal Award address, "that as a boy, when he went to visit the gas works to obtain some hard carbon for his Bunsen cell, this carbon was collected from those parts of the gas retort which had been the hottest, and where the hydrocarbon gas had undergone dissociation, leaving a dense deposit of coherent carbon.

"In this chemical phenomenon of dissociation at high temperature, he perceived a chemical means for 'self-curing' any weak spots in the filament of his lamp. The remedy was as ingenious as simple. In preparing his filament, he passed the current through it while the filament was placed in an atmosphere of hydrocarbon gas, so that in every spot where the temperature rose highest on account of greatest resistance, brought about by the irregular structure of the material, the gas was dissociated and carbon was deposited automatically until the defect was cured."

Here was probably the only way possible to construct a filament of precisely uniform diameter. Nature alone could not do it.

"The next step," said Weston himself, in accepting the Perkin Award, "is to continue the deposition of carbon all over the loop [of the filament], so as to bring the resistance to exactly what you want it before it goes into the lamp. Thus, you have a chemical control of the resistance, not only of the bad spots but of the loop as a whole."

Weston's early method of doing this was as simple as the idea itself. He filled a glass jar with ordinary kerosene oil, then immersed in it a small chemical flask, and filled it. The flask was then inverted, with the neck below the surface of the liquid. Into it Weston carefully inserted a drilled cork, carrying two wires with the filament under treatment fastened between them. The ends of the wires were bent around so that their ends protruded above the kerosene. He then connected a battery to them, with a controlling rheostat, and allowed a weak current to flow.

As the filament warmed up it heated the kerosene in the flask until it began to vaporize and the vapor, collecting in the inverted bottom of the container, drove the oil out into the jar until the filament was exposed to the vapor. When this point was reached, Weston increased the current enough to make the filament glow brightly. At once its weak spots appeared and the vaporized kerosene began to deposit carbon on them. In a few minutes, the spotty nature of the light subsided, and the process was carried on for a predetermined time, to coat the whole length of the wire with hard, shiny carbon.

This was, of course, a crude beginning, and during 1876 and '77 Weston made many improvements in supporting the apparatus and connecting the wires. Eventually he adopted the scheme of electroplating the ends of the filament with copper, to facilitate electrical contacts. As time went on, he abandoned kerosene as too clumsy. When the company began to manufacture incandescent lamps for sale, filaments were lined up in small vertical glass tubes connected in a row to the source of current. The tubes were then pumped down to a partial vacuum and filled with a hydrocarbon gas, and the process was completed as before.

Weston's ingenuity did not stop there. He found that it was necessary to test very delicately for unevennesses in the filament too small to be seen by the eye. To do this he put the filament loop between the poles of a very powerful permanent magnet, and then passed alternating current through the carbon thread. This of course made it vibrate in tune with the alternations of the circuit. If there were any weak spots in its structure, they would show instantly and the filament would quickly break. "That was a severe test," he said, "but it showed us whether we had completely eliminated the defective spots."

It was an interesting sidelight on Weston's scientific method. While everybody else was doing the best he could with fibrous filaments which were sure to develop trouble later on, Weston went them one better and turned out a virtually perfect product of its kind. It was not long before the hydrocarbon method became a basic requirement in the incandescent lamp industry, and was adopted by everyone in one form or another.

"Substantially, every incandescent lamp in the world is made by the process," Weston said. "But there is a curious story in that connection. Who invented it? The courts ruled that I didn't. That is a strange fact. Hiram S. Maxim got the credit for it. Sawyer got the first patent on it. Sawyer and I had a terrible fight over this for a number of years. The courts decided that I had not made the invention. Such are the vicissitudes of an inventor's life. I had made it very early in the history of the work, long before Mr. Maxim or Mr. Sawyer had any knowledge of it whatever."

If this was true, a great injustice has been done. And Weston was never one to take injustice meekly. He did not feel, as many great men do, that he had made enough inventions for which he did get credit, so that this detail, important as it was, could well be surrendered to others. He was mad clean through and went after Sawyer with all the resources at his command.

The legal battle between Weston and Sawyer began in 1882, when Weston saw in the Patent Office Gazette, the notice of a patent granted to Sawyer* on the hydrocarbon idea. He instantly filed an identical patent of his own and brought on an interference action at once. In an interference, the lawyers of each side visit the headquarters of the opposition and hold courts of inquiry, grilling witnesses and examining every possible circumstance in an effort

*Sawyer was associated with another inventor named Man, and the patent was issued to them jointly. But the action was taken against Sawyer alone.

to break down the opponent's claim to priority. Large masses of testimony are taken and a museum of exhibits collected. When it is all done, the evidence is submitted to the Patent Office, and a Trial Examiner, with a board to help him, decides the issue. The winner gets the patent.

Weston's position was weak. The only witnesses he could muster were Edward E. Quimby, his patent attorney, and Levi Broadbent, onetime foreman of his machine shop—and himself. Neither Quimby nor Broadbent could remember accurately when they had first seen Weston experimenting with his hydrocarbon filament treatment. They could not establish the origin of the idea closer than "some time in 1877." As Sawyer and Man had made application for their patent in October, 1878, there was little margin to spare.

But Weston's fiery determination could not be dampened by poor support. In his testimony he gave so accurate and lucid an account of the whole thing that he was completely convincing. The examiners found for him and against Sawyer and Man, and their hydrocarbon patent was thrown out. Weston himself received a patent on the idea in 1884. Sawyer, however, refused to be defeated so easily, and appealed the decision to the civil courts. It was here that the judge eventually ruled against Weston.

By that time everybody was using the "flashing" process, of necessity. Hiram Maxim had come into the picture, and Edison. The decision was at best academic. Though Weston had undoubtedly thought of the process first, a number of others received the idea independently and almost at the same time. Weston, being by nature a lone wolf, had failed to announce his discovery and patent it when he should have. He had preferred to keep it secret, and, being too busy with other profitable things, had simply let it slide.

But the court decision did not do Sawyer much good. He and Weston and everybody else were presently swept overboard by the irresistible wave of Edison's popularity and prestige.

## 16

Weston was not satisfied with a compacted mixture of carbon dust and tar for the making of filaments. At best it produced a grainy material that could never be made entirely homogeneous, even by the hydrocarbon treatment. He wanted something that was *molecularly* smooth and unbroken in texture. Carbon never appeared this way in nature; therefore it would be necessary to go back to charring some form of cellulose, as the others were doing.

But what form of cellulose? Nature was again of no help; there is no form of it that does not grow with a grainy structure. Everyone else had accepted this fact and was making the best of it. Weston declined to do this; he would make a synthetic cellulose product *without* grain.

He set about searching for an absolutely uniform, structureless substance. The search was not immediately successful, and led him through many weeks of discouraging trial and error. But in the end, his skill as a chemist brought him through. The result was a product he called "Tamidine," and a process which gave him lamp filaments far superior to any of his competitors'. So superior, indeed, that the industry adopted it everywhere. When the tungsten filament finally superseded carbon, the Weston homogeneous carbon, in the form of the "squirted filament," had virtually displaced all other materials; practically every one of the millions of light bulbs used by the world contained it.

Weston's own description of his difficulties tells the story with authority and clarity:

I then took up the problem of producing the structureless carbon, a homogeneous thread, of uniform cross section, and of uniform electric resistance from end to end for any given section. This was a chemical problem, of course. At first I attempted to dissolve cellulose. After various expedients, finally including squirting through small openings, I came back to collodion film.

He never forgot anything he had ever done. Now, his early experience with the making of collodion solutions for photographic plates came to his aid.

If you pour a solution of pyroxylin in ether and alcohol on a glass plate it leaves behind a beautiful thin horny film. It has great strength if the cotton from which the collodion is made is good—about 16,000 to 20,000 pounds per square inch. Its tensile strength closely approaches that of some of the poorer metals and some of the rare, good metals. But if you attempt to use a filament of this material for an incandescent lamp, the double solvent causes trouble. The alcohol-ether does not hold the pyroxylin in solution quite as well as it should, and shrinkage and pockmarking happen. We got over that by putting a frame of wood around the glass plate on - which the liquid was poured and covering the top of the frame with a very

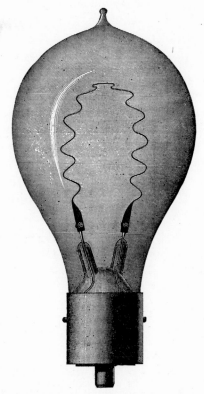

Early Weston incandescent lamp with Tamidine homogeneous filament.

thin but very good filter paper. The vapor of the ether and alcohol traveled slowly through the filter paper and left a perfectly smooth film. Another way was to dissolve the pyroxylin in methyl alcohol and allow the solvent to evaporate. But this absorbed moisture from the atmosphere and caused a precipitate so that the film would turn milky—a result of cooling pyroxylin in a finely divided state in the film—called "chilling" in varnishes. A tray of anhydrous calcium chloride over the plate absorbed the vapor and allowed it to evaporate without the interference of moisture. We finally used ammonium sulphide hydrate to convert the material back again to cellulose.

A great deal of the detail in all this is omitted, but it included many subsidiary discoveries which were then new. Weston was now working in the field which modern chemists call "plastics"—a field which would not be opened for twenty years more. He was encountering some of the mechanical difficulties which even today cause trouble. In fact, he was attempting to manufacture filaments for operation at white heat, out of nothing other than guncotton!

After we got the film in that shape the next thing was to get the gases out of it without getting little explosions in the solid substance. That gave us a lot of trouble. We placed the films in the usual apparatus for baking them and raised the temperature slowly and got films, but the bulk of them would be full of little volcanoes, caused by explosions of gas. We analyzed the gases and then we got along all right. That filament slowly displaced everything else. The process was later modified by squirting cellulose dissolved in chloride of zinc through a very fine tube into alcohol; the homogeneous carbon filaments were obtained and the method was within the limits of the invention as stated in the patent.

Weston was older and wiser now—it was 1882—and lost no time in applying for protection. He and Quimby wrote the patent with utmost care describing the original process, before the squirting method was devised.

If cellulose [says the patent]—that is to say, cotton, cotton waste, linen or paper—be subjected to the action of a mixture of nitric and sulphuric acid, the result is a substance which, though fibrous and possessing in some other respects nearly the same physical qualities as the pure cellulose, differs radically from it, being explosive and burning without appreciable residue when out of contact with the air. This substance is commonly known as "pyroxylin," "guncotton," or "nitro-cellulose." By dissolving this with a mixture of ether and alcohol, collodion is produced. . . . By treating it with various other solvents, such as nitro-benzole, naptha, camphor, and other well-known solvents—the substance known as "celluloid" is produced. Both collodion and celluloid may be formed in thin sheets and dried; but so long as the characteristics of the nitro-cellulose remain they are both unfit for the production of carbons, for the reason that they burn without residue. In order, therefore, to render them suitable for my purpose, I deoxidize them, so to speak, or, in other words, I treat them with such chemical agents as will deprive them of their nitrous qualities and bring them back to the chemical condition of cellulose. Among such reducing agents may be mentioned ammonium sulphide, protochloride of iron, sulphate of iron, and others. The sheets of collodion or celluloid are immersed in a solution containing one or the other of the above-named agents and allowed to remain therein until they are entirely reconverted to their original chemical condition. In many other respects they resemble closely the ordinary celluloid. They become transparent, very tenacious and flexible, and carbonize slightly less readily than ordinary cellulose. From these blanks strips are cut or stamped, having approximately the shape and size desired for the carbon conductors. They are then carbonized by being packed in a closed retort or muffle, between plates of refractory material, and exposed to a high temperature. . . . After carbonization, the strips may be mounted and inserted in the lamps in well-known ways, no further treatment being required.

The patent was granted on September 26, 1882, and became the first real source of wealth to Weston. It was one of his most cherished inventions, this Tamidine. There is no record of the source of the name itself. Presumably, Weston picked it out of the air, as George Eastman was to do with "Kodak" later on. It was a sonorous name and one of the earliest product designations in the electrical business. Weston always delighted in it.

In fact, he always had a specially soft place in his heart for the chemistry of carbon. He was a great friend, for instance, of John Wesley Hyatt, the inventor of celluloid, and kept closely in touch with what might be called the prenatal days of the plastics industry. Out of these earliest patents on plastic incandescent filaments grew the tremendous arts of modern organic chemistry, and in particular the lacquer, rayon, and cellophane branches of those arts.

At the time the Tamidine invention was made, the United States Company was manufacturing incandescent lamps under patents granted to Hiram S. Maxim. These were pretty much the same as Edison's—using carbon filaments made of carbonized fibers. But as soon as Tamidine received patent protection, the company began using it in its standard line of lamps.

An amusing view of the brand-new incandescent system can be gained from a United States Electric Lighting Company catalogue of this early period. The pamphlet is in the nature of an argument. Its front cover carries a lithograph of a nearly naked giant riding the clouds, holding a Weston lamp in one hand and using the supply wires for reins to drive the world. Weston's lighting system is featured prominently next to the light.

"Gas having for years ranked first as an illuminant," says the catalogue with gentle belligerence, "it is only necessary to prove that the incandescent light or glow-lamp is superior to gas . . . for the following reasons:

". . . safest, not only because there is no flame with which articles can come in contact, but also because the use of matches is unnecessary and there is no danger of explosion or suffocation. Furthermore, in case of fire, it adds no fuel to the flames. . . . As it consumes no oxygen, its superiority as a healthful light is undisputed. . . . One gas jet consumes as much oxygen as eight or ten people. If in any office, store or workroom, there should be placed eight or ten people for each gas jet in addition to its regular occupants, who would question the evil results of such crowding?

"Under almost all conditions it is a cheaper light than gas. . . . Properly installed, (incandescent light) can be produced at a cost equal to gas at from 35 cents per 1000 cubic feet."

The catalogue then goes on to say, with a fine sense of modesty, how much better its system is than anybody else's. (This was about as reasonable as its equivalent sales talk is today; everybody was of course saying the same thing.) "Important facts," the catalogue averred, "are that the United States system produces 20 to 40 per cent more candle power per horsepower than others. It affords perfect automatic regulation, so that any number of lamps may be burned with perfect safety to the lamps and dynamo, without requiring the attention of an attendant at the dynamo. Its wiring system is at least 25 percent more economical than competitors'. Its lamp globes do not blacken." (This was a sideswipe at Edison, who had first called attention to the gradual distillation of the carbon filament onto the inside of the bulb. The so-called "Edison effect," however, was beyond the control of Weston or anyobdy else. United States lamps blackened too, but more slowly because the voltage of their system was much lower than Edison's, being about 53 volts.)

These arguments all seem puerile now, since it is hard to believe that gas light ever could have held its own for a day after the first incandescent was lighted. But we must remember how doggedly the world resists *change,* no matter how obvious the improvement offered. Like the accused in ancient law, the new invention is presumed to be guilty until it is proved innocent.

The gas companies, however, were already sufficiently alarmed. They had laughed briefly when news of Edison's "discovery" of the incandescent lamp struck the world. Then they had cautiously examined the threat and now—in the mid-eighties—they were definitely on the run. And, like all men under fire, they were desperately searching for any weapon they could find. It proved to be *Danger.* The electric light was "deadly." The public would become enmeshed in a network of copper cords that would kill on contact . . . It was all very silly, as we see it now, but it led directly into the fantastic period of accusation and counteraccusation, vilification and litigation, out of which only Edison himself emerged free and triumphant.

Tamidine, however, was a major contribution, as important as Edison's own greatest contribution: the high-resistance filament, capable of operating on 100 volts or more. It was so important, indeed, that it rapidly put the United States Company in the lead among all the warring factions. Even Edison knuckled under for a time. There is still among Weston's trophies an envelope containing a browned sheet of a tissue-thin substance that looks like the skin of a mummy. On the outside of the envelope some faithful secretary had written—no doubt at Weston's dictation:

Edison's Pseudotamidine—Received October 5, 1885

This commanding position of the United States Company, based purely on Weston's inventions, made it the major bone of contention in the coming battle of the electrical giants. Both the Edison and Westinghouse interests tried to annex it, and Westinghouse finally did so. It is doubtful whether the latter would have survived without this infusion of new blood. Though Weston did not remain a leading figure in electric lighting, he had inscribed his name on the center of this page in history. He was unquestionably one of the primary inventors of the incandescent lamp, and Tamidine was without doubt his greatest contribution.

Edward F. Weston tells an amusing story of the effect which the invention had on Edison's elaborate search for bamboo. "When a young man," he says, "I personally knew one of [Edison's] emissaries who had covered the island of Japan and part of the mainland of China. He was quite fond of telling me of his experiences in exploring parts of Japan which were practically unknown to white men at that time. His travels were mostly on foot or by jin riksha, and his particular search was for a bamboo fiber. His method was to cut samples from every thicket that he came across, label these as to the point of origin, bundle them up and ship them back to the U.S.

"My friend related how one day he received a cablegram instructing him to abandon his search and return home. When he received these instructions he was much upset because he surmised that some of the other emissaries, who were covering Brazil and other parts of the world, had probably been successful in their quest. Upon reaching home, he received no explanation of the recall, but soon heard that all of his co-workers had also been recalled. This encouraged him somewhat, as he felt that he had at least been as successful as the others. In due time he learned the particulars of the Tamidine filament, and concluded that this was the real reason for his recall."

Of course, Tamidine was not perfect when first invented, and constant work went on in Weston's laboratory to improve it and drive the "bugs" out—get rid of air bubbles, learn to control thickness to the exact six-thousandths of an inch required, work out a production-line hydrocarbon treatment, and so on. One important reason for Tamidine's superiority was that, when carbonized, it had a distinctly higher resistance than the fibrous materials. This permitted larger cross sections for the same voltage and made the filaments mechanically stronger and gave a greater area of incandescence, hence more light per watt of power. Weston's customary method of producing filaments was to place sheets of his reconstituted cellulose in a press and punch out the looped conductors with dies. This gave a beautifully uniform product, but the rectangular cross section of the filament had one disadvantage: it gave an uneven distribution of light. Weston puzzled long over this, finally invented the crinkled filament which was bent in a series of sine waves. This almost entirely corrected the distribution difficulty and made the filament even stronger than before.

Edison's first lamp, tested on October 19–20, 1879, burned out in forty hours. He was jubilant. "That's fine—that's fine!" he cried. "I think we've got it! If it can burn forty hours, I can make it last a hundred." For quite a number of years he and most of the others were content with filaments that lasted a few hundred—and so were the customers. Weston's Tamidine had another story to tell. It was not uncommon for his lamps to burn a total of 2,000 hours!

### 17

The four years from 1882 to 1886 were productive ones indeed for Edward Weston—filled with new ideas for dynamos, arc and incandescent lamps. The patents granted to him in this period represented constant improvements in the fundamental elements of electric power and light. A short résumé of the most important is all that we can consider here.

Although he had devised a successful lamp filament there was still the very serious matter of evacuating the bulb so that the residual oxygen would not consume the carbon. One of his earliest solutions was to construct a lamp with several filaments in it. An ingenious switching device in the interior connected one filament after another, as previous ones burned out. The mechanism was operated by an electromagnet from outside the glass. Needless to say, it was not a practical solution.

More useful was the gas-filled lamp, of which Weston was undoubtedly the original inventor. He made no attempt to exhaust the air, but blew other gases in, gradually displacing the oxygen. Hydrocarbon vapors were his first choice for this, and he later tried nitrogen, then abandoned it as impractical. The gas-filled lamp did not come into favor again till long after Weston had left the field, and did so then because nitrogen, argon, and other inert gases could be produced cheaply and in high purity.

Of considerably greater importance was his invention of the thorium oxide "getter," for cleaning the residual air and occluded gases from lamp bulbs while they were being exhausted. In his patent application of July 12, 1881, he describes it thus: "In carrying out my invention I make use of any ordinary form of incandescent lamp, and in the globe, before it is finally sealed, I introduce a small quantity of a substance possessing the property of absorbing, under certain conditions, air. Such a substance is thorina or thoria, the oxide of the metal thorium, which is used in the following manner: a small quantity being introduced into [the base of] the globe, the latter is connected with the air-exhaust apparatus, and while the air is being withdrawn the thorina is strongly heated. When the exhaustion has been carried as far as possible the heat is withdrawn, the globe detached from the exhaust apparatus and hermetically sealed. On cooling the thorina absorbs the remaining gas or air with such avidity as to leave an almost perfect vaccuum in the globe."

The chemistry of it was simply that, on heating, thorium oxide was broken down into metallic thorium and its oxygen was pumped off with the rest of the air. On cooling, this active metal immediately sought oxygen again and took up what little there was left in the bulb. It is interesting that in this patent Weston speaks of preparing his thorium oxide from ores containing uranium. The uranium, dissolved out with iron and other impurities by means of hydrochloric acid, was thrown away. He was experimenting with the world's most historic metal fifty years before its rise to fame in the atomic bomb.

A second patent, filed later but granted a little sooner, described what he felt was an improvement on this scheme. Here, the inventor showed a row of completed incandescent lamps attached by tubes extending from their tops, to a glass manifold in the form of a T. The bottom of this was connected to the exhaustion pump, while at the side a small retort was sealed into the system, containing thorium oxide. When all possible air was removed, the retort was heated from below and the compound then acted as an absorbent for the residual gases. The advantage as he saw it was that the thorium could thus be saved and used over and over again.

These two patents put Weston clearly in the lead in an invention that has become essential in the making of the billions of modern lamp bulbs and vacuum tubes. If you examine a radio tube, for instance, you will see a slight brownish stain on the inside of the

Manufacture of Weston lamps: exhausting the bulbs and "getting" residual oxygen.

glass at one point. This is the "getter"—the thorium and thorium oxide mentioned by Weston. The silvery sheen is the excess of pure thorium left after all the oxygen has been combined. In the case of vacuum tubes not intended for lighting, it is cheaper now to put a small charge of the chemical inside, heat it with a special filament during evacuation. Lamp bulbs are still made by a modification of the manifold principle shown in Weston's second patent.

While the thorium scrubbing technique became a standard part of lamp-manufacturing procedure, Weston still needed a better way to obtain a good vacuum. He had been trying for years to get a good pump, without very happy results. There were two kinds—the mechanical piston pump, working in oil, and the Sprengel mercury pump. As he began work on incandescents in 1876, nothing was available but the mechanical type, and he bought one after another of these, only to find them ineffective. Even now, the best laboratory mechanical pump can only produce a "rough" vacuum, because of leaks and the fact that the lowest possible pressure obtainable is no lower than the vapor pressure of the oil itself. It is used today only as a means of assisting the diffusion pumps, which do the principal work.

As late as 1879 Weston was still hunting for a satisfactory air pump, and commissioned a New York importing firm to find "the best vacuum pump made in Europe." The importers corresponded with Swan in England, the foremost incandescent lamp inventor east of the Atlantic, but no pump was forthcoming until Dr. Richards, a consultant of the firm, went abroad himself. Weston asked him to see Swan, and also Gimmingham, who was making pumps for Sir William Crookes. Richards did so, but the Swan pump he brought home a year later was inferior to the ones Weston already had. Finally, in 1881, Weston "inherited" a group of skillful German mechanics with the laboratory of the United States Electric Lighting Company, and these men made him a pump that gave reasonably good results. It was of the mechanical type, for the Sprengel mercury pump could not care for anything but small capacity. It was not till many decades later that Dr. Irving Langmuir brought out his improved mercury diffusion pump, which drove the air out of a space by bombarding its molecules with mercury vapor from a jet, discharging them into a trap kept at low pressure by a mechanical pump. The diffusion principle, in various forms, has now become the standard method of obtaining high vacuum. In "alpha" and "beta" processes used in the separation of the uranium isotopes in the recent atom bomb project, gigantic steel tanks of hundreds of cubic feet capacity were kept exhausted by diffusion pumps to a vacuum *far higher* than any found in modern electric lamps.

But Weston was unable to accept the Sprengel pump without trying to improve upon it. The most objectionable thing about it was that the mercury, having fallen to the bottom of a tube into a beaker, had to be raised and poured again by hand. Weston sought to make this operation automatic, redesigning it so that a set of heating coils vaporized the mercury in a lower chamber and raised it to a reservoir on top. This gave continuous circulation.

He got several patents on his improvements, among them a rearrangement of the tubes, which gave a better air seal and produced considerably higher vacua. These changes have become standard in this type of pump, although it is still known as Sprengel's invention.

### 18

To obtain a high vacuum was one thing; to keep it intact in the bulb for months or years was another—and equally important. Everybody working in the incandescent field had to provide some kind of a seal where the lead-in wires passed from the lamp base through the glass. The common practice was to fix a couple of small platinum wires in place with the bulb stem hot, then crimp them tight. Metal and glass had coefficients of expansion so nearly alike that the seal did not separate when it cooled. At least, that was the hope, and all patents described some variation of this method.

Weston, as usual, went at the matter from a scientific rather than an inventive standpoint, using his broad technical knowledge to help him. His own patent on incandescent lamp seals, dated March 21, 1882, was an ingenious one indeed, and gave him a highly satisfactory solution to the problem. The bottom of the lamp bulb was made separately, in the form of a glass cup, through which two small glass tubes protruded above and below. The process consisted of fitting into the tubes a pair of copper wires of the same diameter as the bore. At the lower ends, both glass and copper were painted with a mixture of platinum chloride and oil of lavender. Moderately heated, the organic compound picked up the chloride radical and left a thin film of pure platinum coating the joint. This was then exposed to a high temperature, fusing a thin layer of the metal securely to the glass. The platinum was then electroplated with copper till it was strong enough to resist atmospheric pressure, giving a continuous seal between wires and glass. The whole operation could be performed on a long row of lamp bases in a few minutes.

Carbon filament loops were now attached to each pair of lead-in wires and secured either by riveting or electroplating methods. Then the cups were welded to the lower opening of the bulbs, and the lamps were complete.

This ingenious system was adopted for all the company's lamps, and worked perfectly. But the patent succumbed, like every other of the same kind, to the irresistible Edison. The great inventor's wizardly attorney, in writing the original incandescent patent, claimed only two things: the sealing of conductors into a glass bulb, and the closing off of the bulb itself after exhausting the air. The courts decided that Edison had covered all possible methods of making a permanent seal. And since no one could make a commercially practicable lamp without a durable vacuum, every patent in the field was declared an infringement of Edison's. In the general debacle that followed, Weston lost not only his sealing patent but his hydrocarbon and Tamidine patents as well. Nobody in America could make an incandescent lamp that would work, without paying royalty to Edison's commercial heirs for the use of the vacuum bulb!

Fortunately, Weston did not anticipate this sweeping decision, and he went on, during the eighties, making valuable inventions, as others were doing, and thus greatly benefiting the art and rendering great service to future millions who would use the electric light.

Among his minor patents of this period appeared one that overcame a serious annoyance—the heating of the ends of the lead-in wires where they were joined to the carbon filament ends. The incandescent carbon often overheated or even fused the wires, destroying the joints and ending the life of the lamp. It was customary to add carbon washers at the points of connection or to attempt to enlarge the carbon filaments there. These were difficult and expensive methods and not very satisfactory. The Weston patent described an alternate, and much simpler, method. It consisted merely of *increasing the density* of the filament ends so as to make them more conductive and hence less heated in service. In the case of Tamidine, cut filaments were reinforced at their ends with more of the same material, then pressed to the same cross section throughout. A short end section was thus given a much greater density.

This invention also worked so well that it was adopted for all the United States Company's lamps.

### 19

The year 1884 found Weston in the full swing of the electric lighting tide, riding high and far out front. He now decided that incandescent lamps could properly compete with the arc light for *outdoor* illumination, and set about producing a "mammoth" lamp. The candle-power rating of this was 125, something like eight times as much as the standard Edison lamp. People told him that it would be impossible to build. This quantity of light seems trifling now, with modern tungsten filaments producing light intensities in the thousands of candle power. But it must be remembered that candle power is not a measure of total light but only of *the intrinsic brilliance* of the source, so that Weston's new lamp did indeed represent an advance of eight times in the effectiveness of his filaments.

The mammoth lamp was not merely an enlargement of the ordinary size; everything about it had to be redesigned—filament, globe, base, connections. It consumed 2.3 amperes at 160 volts and turned out to be far more efficient than standard sizes. It was a third to a half as powerful a source of light as the arc. But it had so many advantages that it was rapidly adopted for factories and public halls and did actually appear on the streets. Said the *Scientific American:* "Unlike arc lights [the Weston lamp] casts no shadows"—meaning no shadows produced by its own structure—"and requires no attention. There is no pulling up and down every day and renewing of carbons; the lamp is simply switched on and off. . . ."

In addition to the lower cost for attendance, said the *Electrical Review*, "the incandescent lamp has a considerable advantage in distribution and utilization of the light produced. Much of the light from an arc lamp is dissipated in directions where its effects are not useful, owing to the impossibility of properly adjusting reflectors to the constantly shifting arc." All the light from the incandescent, Weston found, could be readily directed downward by simple white shades. For the first time, also, street lighting could be run on the multiple system, with each light independent of every other.

Incandescent lighting for streets began in the early eighties, and it was Weston's mammoth lamps that first appeared. By means of a "series-multiple" system of wiring, he could operate at reasonably high voltages and low currents and yet avoid the troubles inherent in the single-circuit arc system. He invented relays and automatic rheostats to substitute resistance equal to a lamp when it burned out. These devices were built into the shades over the lights. William Stevens, who had been his faithful right-hand man ever since 1875, worked out some of the details.

In 1884, the Franklin Institute in Philadelphia put on an electrical exhibition, which gathered together the latest apparatus of all sorts. After the exhibition had closed, the Institute proceeded to make comparative tests on dynamos and electric lighting systems for the benefit of the competing companies. In the lighting field the testing committee, headed by Professor W. D. Marks of the University of Pennsylvania, drew up a set of rules outlining rather severe life tests on twenty lamps from each competitor. Edison and the United States Company were among those who entered their product.

When preliminary testing was begun on the Tamidine lamps, it was at once apparent that they were inferior, lighting unevenly and varying widely in resistance and current demand. Weston, who had been extremely busy with other matters, suddenly heard that the tests were going wrong and wrote a hurried letter to Marks. "I commenced an investigation of the matter," he said, "and soon found that you had been supplied with a singularly bad lot of lamps,

Weston's exhibit at the Franklin Institute, Philadelphia, 1884.

the defect being due to imperfect baking of the loops (filaments). The resistance of the loops will rise rapidly and the lamps will fail in such a short time as to leave no doubt in your mind that if we made such lamps regularly we could not possibly continue to do business."

He had been away from Newark; no one at the plant had taken pains to inspect the lamps to be tested in Philadelphia.

Weston now asked for a second test, and got it, with the same unfavorable results. He then wrote Marks that "it is useless to spend any time on the lamps of our make which you now have," and requested that the defective lamps be thrown out and good ones substituted. The committee would have complied, but Francis Upton, Edison's chief engineer, protested strongly and insisted the tests go on with the original Weston Tamidine lamps. It was an opportunity not to be missed. Weston protested this, but the committee decided that Upton was right, and the life tests and photometric measurements continued. Several conferences in person with them did not change their minds.

Weston's difficulty soon got into the press, and the technical journals quickly took sides. Among other things it was discovered that the Tamidine lamps had been bought by the committee in Boston, out of regular dealer's stock, while most of the Edison lamps had come directly from the factory, it being known they were intended for technical tests. The Edison company had a rule that lamps could not be sold unless the purchaser stated what he was going to use them for!

Tests began in April, 1885, with four companies competing. All lamps in the competition were guaranteed to last 600 hours. In June, when the trials had run continuously for 1064 hours, the scores were taken. Edison had won hands down, with only one lamp of his twenty failing. Weston had lost seventeen. The Stanley lamp, made by the Thomson-Houston Company, had lost nineteen. An English firm was little better off, with eleven, (which was all they had entered). But this latter company had shown the best average efficiency, with Weston next and Edison a poor last. In 1000 hours his lamps had lost half their candle power.

The affair was infuriating to Weston, and produced an entering wedge between him and the United States Company, which rapidly split them apart. The profession did not blame him for the poor lamps; this was understood to be carelessness in manufacture. Actually, he had become so thoroughly expert in the illuminating art that he was named a member of a committee to determine a better method of standardizing upon the efficiency and output ratings of electric lamps. In this connection he advocated a new type of spherical photometric measurement which did not find favor with his associates. The old system of measuring light intensity merely in the horizontal plane was retained.

Eventually, the spherical system was adopted. Today, nobody would think of measuring a lamp in any other way.

20

Until the year 1886, Edward Weston worked day and night for the advance of the commercial lighting art. His fame had spread throughout the land. Not only had he become one of the great pioneers in electrical engineering, but he was known, too, as the most formidable adversary that any man could have in court. He had met practically all of his competitors in infringement or interference battles, and had ousted them all, including Edison. He had not won every time, but nobody denied that if an electrical subject were under discussion, Weston was likely to know more about it than anybody else.

And this was not strange, for he had taken a more scientific view of the whole field than any other inventor who was engaged in a commercial enterprise. He was, at heart, a laboratory man, not a promoter, and his laboratory procedure was the most highly developed in the country. Out of his work rooms had come many of the fundamental theories of electrical engineering.

Weston was at least the equal of Brush in fathering the arc light, and his superior in pushing its development to the practical stage. He had invented one of the most successful incandescent lamps and had given the world two basic elements of it: the non-fibrous filament and the method of "flashing" to eliminate weak spots. He had also invented the technique of "getting" the residual gas in a bulb. All three of these were permanently absorbed into the art.

He had produced many lesser inventions also, in order to make his electric systems complete: switches, regulators, rheostats, fixtures, brackets, fuses—everything from a minor arrangement on an electric lamp support to whole systems of wiring for a community. In this, of course, he was not unique. Every electrical pioneer had to do the same thing, making his system complete without outside help, in order to avoid being eliminated from the race altogether. Weston simply had more fundamental knowledge to support his ingenuity than most of the others. He lacked, however, the great dramatizing power that Edison possessed, and his inventions of this period were largely submerged thereby.

By mid-1886 Weston had been granted 186 patents, a worthy record indeed.

He had been an important pioneer, too, in establishing electric central-station service. Weston electric light companies reached all the way from Brooklyn to Denver and San Francisco, from Alabama to Canada, and were found in France and many other foreign countries, too.

When Edison was still struggling to open his famous Pearl Street generating plant in New York in 1882, Weston was quietly opening the Weston Electric Lighting Station for the Newark Electric Light and Power Company on Mechanic Street. Distribution was by overhead wires, at the voltage actually used in the lamp circuit. More than 300 arcs were supplied. The station consisted of a large "hall" in which as many as forty-eight dynamos were installed in four rows, based on wooden frames like double saw horses. Overhead, as many pulleys whirred, as they drove the dynamos through a forest of individual belts. At the rear the giant flywheel of a 300-horsepower steam engine kept the whole thing in motion. The boiler house was built directly behind the power room. There were no switchboards, merely small boxes along the wall containing cutouts and regulator mechanisms. The dynamo of this period was not the ring-frame machine which Weston had applied to electroplating. It was a massive and rather ugly affair with a rectangular frame supporting

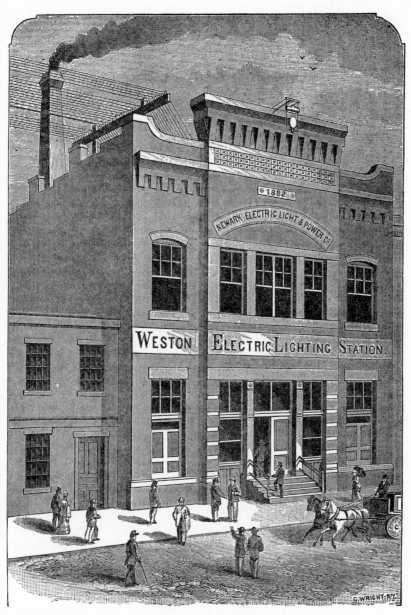

Weston "central station."

four field magnets. Pole shoes were in the middle, with the armature centered between them.

Beautiful or not, this machine was considerably more sensible in design than the "Long Waisted Mary Anns" which Edison still insisted were necessary to obtain effective magnetic field circuits.

The United States Company's catalogue claimed the highest efficiency of dynamos and lights of any system on the market; they probably made good on this boast. They were frankly competing with gas and even had the temerity to suggest that the gas companies themselves might like to enlarge their income by installing a few electric light plants.

Gas men knew they were being pushed to the wall, and prepared to fight accordingly. In Newark, they attempted to obtain a monopoly franchise for all lighting, from the City Council, by a route now long familiar. "Considerable indignation has been aroused in Newark, N. J.," said a contemporary engineering journal, "over the proposition of the gas companies to reduce the price of their product to the citizens as well as the city, provided they are protected in their monopoly for a period of ten years. As Newark may be called the home of the Weston system of lighting, the United States Company will no doubt jealously guard the interests of the people in its efforts to obtain a firm foothold for the electric light."

The company did indeed do that, and within two years was itself buying up a competitor and becoming an even bigger monopoly than the gas company had been. But this is the necessary way with public utilities.

For a time in Newark, gas prevailed because it was cheaper than arcs. But presently gas could not be given away to store owners. Electricity at any price was worth it. The price was no bargain, however; 75 cents for each arc lamp burning till midnight, and a dollar for all night; another dollar for day lamps. Incandescents were not much easier on the customer. It cost them 1¼ cents an hour for each lamp.

There were two sides to this bargain, though. The City of New York extracted an indemnity of $1.40 for each light that failed to burn the night through.

The *Electrical World* reported upon an amusing reason why

hotels were clamoring for electric lights to replace gas, even at the exorbitant rates. The villain in the piece was the drummer, whose endless travels had taught him to beat the game in every possible way.

The drummer, ever alert for any scheme to further his own interests, has adopted a plan to "get even," as he calls it, with the hotels. Every one of them carries gas burners and a pair of pliers to put them on brackets or chandeliers. The average hotel gas burner is of three-foot size, that is, burning about that number of feet per hour, which gives ample light for rooms under ordinary circumstances. But the drummer is not satisfied with this. He unscrews the three-foot tip and replaces it with his own six- or eight-foot burner, which he lights just as soon as he gets to his room, and lets it blaze away all night, giving enough light to illuminate a hall and sufficient heat to warm the room. . . . With electricity this trick is done away with and a big saving is made.

Nowadays, it is towels and silver.

The early arc-lighting systems were not without their dangers, and the gas companies at least did nothing to *prevent* the circulation of gruesome stories of sudden death. New York reacted rather violently, at first, against what was undoubtedly the carelessness of the lighting companies. In 1888, when broad use of current was just beginning to make personal danger a problem, a report ran: "At the inquest of a young man who was killed in a Bowery clothing store through touching an arc lamp, the jury's verdict censured the United States Illuminating Company [a subsidiary] for having lamps in a position that makes them dangerous to the public, and for not having their lamps and wires insulated. It also recommends all electric light companies to insert a clause in their contracts with patrons, warning them not to touch the lamps and wires."

As late as 1895, death was still stalking the wires. Franklin L. Pope, an engineer of Great Barrington, Mass., and a long-time colleague and friend of Weston's, accidentally made contact with wires leading to a transformer in his cellar. Two thousand volts killed him instantly. This was one of the early alternating-current installations, invented by William Stanley, who had made his first a-c transmission experiments in Great Barrington. Edward Weston went there with a committee from the American Institute of Electrical Engi-

Interior of Weston's Newark station.

neers to investigate, reconstructed every detail of the tragedy, and reported the system to be dangerous. The case got tremendous publicity and was a large factor in forcing the safety code for wiring and grounding, which men like Elihu Thomson had been urging for years without result.

Just how panicky the public could be about a thing they did not understand is shown by a story of the early arc lamps unearthed long afterward by H. L. Mencken and published in his book *Newspaper Days*. A lazy Baltimore reporter, it seemed, was about to be fired one rainy Sunday night unless he brought in a lively story. Finding that there was nothing more newsworthy at the Police Department than a runaway horse and two lost children, he fell to contemplating a row of brilliant arc lamps hung outside the shops. It occurred to him that if a man soaked to the skin should prod one of the lights with the metal point of his umbrella, he might get an interesting shock.

Next morning, a headline story appeared, describing just such an incident, in which an unfortunate visitor from Washington, William T. Benson, had tried the experiment and had landed in the Baltimore hospital. The reporter kept his job—until 200 merchants hastily removed their arc lamps. "By noon," says Mencken, "the number was close to a thousand. By 3 P.M., the lawyers of the electric company were closeted with the business manager of the *Herald,* and his veins were running ice water at their notice of a libel suit for $500,000. They were ready to prove in court that it was impossible to get a shock from one of their lights."

The newspaper got no satisfaction by checking up on the story. There was no record of any Benson at the hospital; the only man of that name in Washington had not been to Baltimore for nine years. Clearly there was no possible defense. But frenzied attempts to repudiate the story as a hoax did not stop the complainants, who had soon fixed a date for the trial. And the merchants were not reassured; they feared that such an accident might really occur.

There was no trial. For, on the eve of the day of its opening, which also happened to be rainy, "a man carrying a steel-rodded umbrella lifted it to clear another pedestrian's umbrella in West Baltimore Street and the ferrule touched the lower carbon socket of one of the few surviving arc lights. When the cops got him to the hospital he was dead."

Nevertheless, the electric light companies were doing well, and the United States Company especially so. By the middle of 1885 they had 23,000 horsepower of generating equipment in service, in the hands of subsidiary lighting companies far and wide. They had lighted the Brooklyn Bridge, many hundred miles of city streets, thousands of stores, homes, and hotels. Their business was well on the road to a million dollars a year. And practically all of this was the result of the Weston dynamo and Tamidine filament, with some help from Hiram Maxim's ingenious hand.

At thirty-six, Edward Weston had established himself as a successful pioneer; he had done work enough to last a lifetime. And he was on the way to being rich. But he was not satisfied. Electric lighting and power were no longer in their infancy; the ground breaking had been done.

He was restless. He wanted new fields to conquer. So he decided to strike out for himself. On the first of July, 1886, he resigned and became once more a lone eagle.

The Weston Factory at Plane and Orange Streets, Newark.

# PART FOUR

# The Measurer

---

## I

On the first of July, 1886, Weston departed from the United States Electric Lighting Company in something more than a huff. In fact, it was the culminating act in a long, bitter wrangle with George W. Hebard, president of the company. Since the beginning of the year Weston had been growing more and more dissatisfied with the way the officials were handling the company's affairs. Though he did not have specific authority to direct the business, he never hesitated to voice criticisms when he had them. Having many, he proceeded to precipitate a number of very painful interviews, both in his laboratory and in the president's office. It ended by his becoming a sworn enemy of Hebard and various other officers. He even carried the feud into his social life.

Typically, Weston identified personal animosity with business criticism. Not approving of Hebard's way of running the company, he also disapproved of Mr. Hebard himself, and violently. Being stormy of nature, and so very sure of himself, Edward Weston put his whole heart into the fight. All that spring of 1886, he made it his principal object in life to best the company's management. He failed.

His contention was that Hebard was more interested in manipulating the stock of the company in Wall Street than in selling electrical goods on a highly competitive market. Before Weston's dynamo company had merged with the United States Company, the latter had operated principally in New York City, where a "reign of extravagance" had been indulged by the directors. Fancy salaries had gone to these men for doing very little about the business. After consolidation, the reign had continued. The cost of making sales, so Weston charged, was actually greater than the profits. Hebard and his friends, manipulating the stock on the strength of Weston's reputation, were making big money, while many of the inventor's friends—and he himself—were in effect paying the bill, by failing to receive dividends.

Weston repeatedly confronted Hebard with these allegations, and Hebard steadily denied them. The Englishman got madder and madder, and the less satisfaction he received from his superior, the harder he worked to unearth proof of his malfeasance. It began to affect Weston's health. He became irritable and preoccupied, he slept less and less, and eventually stood on the brink of a nervous breakdown. It ended with a physical collapse.

A second irritant was Maxim, who had been more or less displaced when Weston joined the company. Maxim's brain was fantastically prolific, and he had become a constant liability for the odd reason that he invented improvements in the company's products so fast that he was forever making them obsolete. Since the company was not big enough for two such inventors, he was finally persuaded to return to England, where he became the driving force in the Maxim-Weston Company, Ltd., spreading the application of electric lighting through Great Britain and the Continent.

Weston's resignation in 1886 was by no means the end of the imbroglio, as it was called by the technical press. He went right on trying, for the next two years, to reform the United States Company by remote control, fighting doggedly to protect the interests of the minority stockholders. This was further complicated by the fact that, upon resigning, he had signed a new contract, becoming "consulting electrician" to the firm. Such an arrangement was necessary, because virtually everything the concern made was covered by Weston patents assigned to them on a royalty basis. Development of Weston dynamos and lights virtually ceased when he quit. Hebard was forced to deal with him or go out of business.

The dealings were not pleasant. For months the two men wrote each other angrily, wrangling over the amount of royalties to be paid. The argument was never settled satisfactorily, but an act of God finally put an end to it. But that is perhaps unfair to the Deity, for the cause was plain carelessness. On Friday, June 17, 1887, the

Newark lampworks burned down, temporarily putting the company out of business in that field. According to a contemporary journal:

The fire broke out in the laboratory, and spread rapidly through the entire building. Most of the building was occupied by the manufacture of carbon filaments and glass globes for incandescent lights. Owing to the inflammable nature of the contents of the works and the delay in sending out an alarm, the whole structure was in flames when the engines arrived.

A second and third alarm were sent out on the arrival of Chief Kierstead, and the entire department of the city was soon at the scene. It required, however, the hardest work on the part of the firemen to save the new main building.

The entire building in which the fire started, occupying about 230 feet of Orange Street and 100 feet on Plane Street, and the engine house, which is situated in the center of the block, together with their contents, were entirely destroyed, the walls falling in about two hours after the fire started. The loss is estimated at $150,000, which is covered by insurance. One hundred and fifty hands are thrown out of employment by the fire.

Insurance could cover the physical loss, but it could not replace the lost time. In the fierce battle then raging with Edison for commercial supremacy, the United States Company was hopelessly crippled. It never recovered, and eventually went bankrupt. When Westinghouse bought the remains, it was largely Weston's designs and what were left of his lamp patents, that constituted their purchase.

Weston's resignation had indirectly caused the fire. During his tenure, he had carefully stored all Tamidine in the damp cellar of the building, thoroughly protected. But after his departure, stacks of the raw sheet material were moved up to the first floor to be more handy, and stored in cardboard cases on high shelves in the hottest part of the room. Electric wires directly behind them presumably short-circuited and set off what amounted to a guncotton explosion.

2

Weston never forgave Hebard for his mismanagement. As late as 1898 he was still telling his friends about the iniquities of his former associates. This was not peculiar to Weston, however. Almost every inventor in those early days was victimized by the sharp businessmen of the times, and many a bitter feud stained the memory of the pioneers long after they had retired full of honors.

In terminating the work that had absorbed his entire days and much of his nights for nine years, Weston did not end his usefulness to the electrical arts. In fact, it was one of those unhappy breaks in a man's life that leads quickly to something even more important. Immediately his resignation was in and his health somewhat restored, he was eagerly sought by almost every opposing inventor as an expert witness in the cutthroat patent suits then raging. He asked and was cheerfully given fees as high as the most expensive experts, such as his friend Pope, and in a short time, having to refuse offers from sheer lack of time, got even better figures. Several companies gave him a yearly retainer for furnishing court assistance when it was needed.

The stage was now set for the "Battle of the Century" in electric lighting. In 1885, the Edison Electric Light Company decided to go after everybody at once, and in that year instituted twenty-six suits. The United States Electric Lighting Company headed the list. "As the suits in these cases are for the determination of absolute ownership by patent of the right to control the essential principles of incandescent lighting," said the *Electrical World,* "their issue involves the question of the existence of the companies and affects in this way, $15,000,000 of invested capital." The action, decided the *Scientific American,* "is on a scale which promises to give a large number of lawyers a fine field of labor."

It would indeed, and with it, an equally fine field for expert witnesses, of which Edward Weston was sure to be one.

Weston combined two invaluable talents as a technical witness: He could express himself with force and clarity, and his memory for the chaotic history of electric power and lighting was as detailed as a printed catalogue. He was a tower of strength, and was loved by his own side and respected by the opposition. He would never accept a job as a witness unless he believed his employer's cause to be just.

But for all his proficiency in court he could not prevail in the Edison lamp suits, and eventually lost everything he had done in respect to incandescent lamps.

Late in the eighties, the United States Company brought a counter suit against Edison for infringement of Weston's hydrocarbon patent. This seemed like sure ground on which to strike back at the successful giant. The suit dragged on for four years, being repeatedly postponed because of legal maneuvers and crowded court calendars. The decision was not handed down till 1892, and was in favor of Edison.

The United States Company immediately appealed the case to a higher court—and was slapped down again, this time for good.

Weston himself had not testified in his own behalf, refusing to have anything to do with his former associates. It is interesting to note that Edison got little or nothing from his victory. By this time he had been pretty much eliminated from the growing combine of the electric light—in all but name.

In 1893 Weston made the wrangle the subject of an address at a National Electric Light Association convention in St. Louis. "They applied to me for assistance," he said, referring to the United States Lighting people, "which for just reason was refused, and they went to argument with a case which was essentially weak in every point where it could easily have been made conclusive. . . . I can truly say that I have honestly endeavored to discover the existence of any moral qualities in some electric light companies, and failed to find any. In this particular matter, the course of both parties would bring a blush of shame to the face of an honest man."

Why he did not get into the fight and make it an honest one, he did not explain.

3

In the summer of 1886 Weston entered the work for which his name has become a household word—the science of electrical measurement. Like everybody else in the field he had been plagued by the lack of simple and accurate measuring instruments for testing dynamos, motors, and lights, and for determining the quantity of electricity which customers used and should be charged for. He determined now to go to the root of the matter and devise a reliable means of doing these things.

Having a comfortable income from the royalties on his numerous inventions, he built himself a large laboratory at the back of his Newark home, now on fashionable High Street, above the main part of town. It consisted of a remodeled wooden building with a good-sized brick addition, and a small boiler room in between. A beautifully ornate Armington & Sims high-speed steam engine occupied a prominent place in the main building. The manufacturers had made him a present of it. Belted to this was a five-horsepower dynamo of his own make, wired for lighting the laboratory and supplying motors for machines and ventilating fans.

All kinds of light machine tools were present, including an accurate set of rolls for shaping thin metal. There were lathes, shapers, milling machines, planers, and drills—everything that the best "model room" in a large factory might have. Nearby benches abounded in hand tools of every description, both for metal and wood. Weston had made a special effort to obtain the finest gauges of all sorts, for he intended to do precision work of the highest order. He was tired of the limitations imposed upon an inventor by slipshod workmanship and lack of equipment.

In still another part of the laboratory was a chemical department. Here again, he had specialized in delicate balances and testing devices. But the place also included shelves and cabinets wonderfully stocked with every substance he could possibly need. Gas pipes and electric wiring were conveniently placed near the work benches.

Nearby was a companion physical laboratory, including everything that had been devised for analysis and measurement—resistance coils, galvanometers, photometers, spectroscopes, and photographic and magic-lantern equipment.

Office space was also provided, and the inventor immediately set up a complete system of records, data books, and drawing files. And lastly, he had collected a library of no less than 10,000 volumes.

Within a few months he was regularly employing as many as five men, and often more. His weekly payroll ran as high as $100.

This unique private laboratory was the expression of the successful scientist—such an outlay as most of his contemporaries dreamed of but never attained. It symbolized Edward Weston accurately— the pioneer of middle age, who had won his spurs and his fortune by signal contributions to an infant art, and who now, at the age

The measuring room in Weston's private laboratory.

of forty-six, intended to go on into the realms of near-perfection. Every room and every shelf bespoke the determined, self-willed man who knew exactly what he wanted and was supremely confident that he knew how to attain it.

But this laboratory was more than that: it was, indeed, the fore-runner, the "pilot plant," of the great industrial laboratories for pure research—institutions which businessmen would not deem valuable for at least another decade.

In December of that year Weston dedicated the laboratory by inviting the Society of Mechanical Engineers to visit him during their annual convention in New York. "The visitors were greatly pleased with what they saw," remarked the *Electrical World,* primly. But the editors of technical magazines all over the United States hastened to send their reporters to get the story of the laboratory. It was a landmark in American engineering. Weston was thoroughly pleased, in his unexpressive way. He had at last attained independence from commercial worries, and had in his hands the implements to make real and satisfying progress.

Soon he had begun a regime of experiment that kept him at work for as much as fifteen to twenty hours a day. "I have often known him to work," said his secretary, "all during the night and not leave his laboratory in time to dress for breakfast. He was the hardest working man I have ever known." One of the things which helped to crowd his time was a steady stream of lecture engagements and the reception at the laboratory of students from the engineering colleges everywhere. Cornell, Sibley, the Franklin Institute, Stevens, and many more heard him on electrometallurgy, lighting, and power, and their professors of engineering sent delegations of students to visit him in return.

4

Weston now began upon an intensive study of electrical measurements, determined to continue methodically until he had reduced a chaotic situation to an orderly art. This was not a new field to him, nor to many other scientists, principally Europeans. Every inventor of an electric system had had to have measuring devices, and a crude beginning had been made upon their design and construction. But even after fifteen years of experiment there was little agreement as to principles. Nearly everybody who needed instruments was forced to make them for himself, or buy them in crude and bulky form in Europe.

In 1886 the crying need was for devices to measure the large voltages and currents of electric power. Portable meters had never been heard of. All instruments of the day depended upon the interaction of a circuit carrying the current and a movable iron piece, or a magnetic needle influenced by the earth's field. The coil carried current from the circuit to be measured; the magnetism was provided either by a permanent magnet or by the earth's natural field. They were all clumsy and inaccurate.

Hans Christian Oersted produced the first measuring instrument in 1819—a large ring of wire with a magnetic needle swinging inside it. This principle was seized upon and improved by many others, until the "galvanometer" emerged as a fairly reliable device. But it was extremely bulky and delicate. For the first three decades of electrical application, telegraphy was the only art in need of measurement. Its voltages were fairly high but its currents were minute; both could be readily measured with some type of galvanometer. The most important thing in telegraphy was a line without leaks, that is, with high resistance to ground. The British scientists, particularly Wheatstone, had devised extraordinarily effective means of determining faults in lines. These methods were brought almost to perfection by Thomson, Varley, and others, for use on the great Atlantic cable. The siphon recorder, the quadrant electrometer and the string galvanometer, with its tiny mirror supported on a hair-like quartz thread, have scarcely been surpassed. Thomson, in one marvelous demonstration with his siphon recorder, received signals after they had traveled through six thousand miles of cable. The current was supplied by a single voltaic cell made of a thimble, with a few drops of acid and tiny fragments of metal for electrodes.

It was a shocking fact that when the electrical art turned to the use of "brute force," there was nothing available for making measurements but superdelicate instruments of this type.

All of the early dynamo makers ran into the same difficulty: To test their machines they had to set up elaborate galvanometers, spend hours adjusting them, then apply mathematical formulas to the readings they took in order to reduce them to simple electrical units.

In his own laboratory in 1886, Weston installed a large and highly accurate tangent galvanometer in a special room. It had a six-foot semicircle of wood, with a scale inscribed inside the curve. Its suspended mirror and magnetized needle were held in the zero position by the earth's field. When the current to be measured, passed through a surrounding coil it set up an opposing field and deflected the needle until the two fields balanced. The angle of deflection was then read on the scale and used to compute the value of the current. Successful operation depended upon absolute stillness and the absence of all stray magnetic influences. No one could carry a pocket knife nearby, or even enter the room with nails on his shoes.

Weston had a trusted assistant named Young, whose job it was to go on scouting expeditions for special supplies. Every few days Young would return to the laboratory to report. Whenever he dropped into the galvanometer room the big instrument would go crazy. So they would send him outside, first to take off his shoes, then his iron-rimmed spectacles. It did no good. Mr. Young's presence was fatal to the instrument. His friends finally decided that he was personally magnetic, and whenever he came along, word would go around jokingly to close down the measuring room.

This phenomenon appealed to Weston as a mystery worth solving. Painstakingly he searched Young for bits of steel, got his suspenders away and removed the iron buttons from his pants. Still no good. At last, however, the mystery was cleared. Young wore a battered derby hat. Inside it was a thin iron-wire stiffener.

The work Weston had first planned to do in his new quarters was not on instruments but on delicate measurements of the light distribution of arc lamps and on the efficiency of his dynamos. But he soon found that, even in the absence of Mr. Young, it was taking him more time to adjust his few instruments and convert their readings into useful data than to apply the results to further experiments. He would perhaps have continued to put up with this annoyance a while longer if he had not had a practical demonstration of its seriousness at that moment.

The Franklin Institute, in the fall of 1886, held a second electrical exhibition and included a large booth of Weston's inventions, among them several dynamos. It was necessary to make careful tests of these machines before the opening, and this took a full week. The only instrument for measuring voltage and current was the tangent galvanometer. Most of the week was wasted in setting it up, leveling it, and calibrating it. Among other things, the earth's magnetic field had to be determined—a factor which can easily vary from day to day under the influence of magnetic storms generated by the sun. To obtain reliable data from such an instrument was a matter of purest chance. Weston came back from Philadelphia thoroughly exasperated, feeling for the first time in his life that he was blocked by the inadequacy of the tools at hand. He resolved to carry through to a conclusion the invention of a satisfactory new measuring device —something he had often worked on in spare moments but had never finished.

Edison, Brush, Elihu Thomson, and Weston himself all had makeshift indicators to go with their dynamos. Edison's first method of measuring the current that was going out of his power stations was to hang a shingle nail on a string near one of the feeder wires. As the current built up, its increasing magnetic field pulled the nail more and more out of the vertical. When it had swung a certain distance Edison would adjust his generators till the lamps in the station seemed to be "going about right." This was his only test for operating voltage in 1882. A little later on he invented the electrolytic meter, which was the earliest watt-hour indicator. Part of the load current was diverted through a jar of zinc-sulphate solution, containing two zinc plates. Zinc was removed from one plate and deposited on the other in proportion to the amount of current used in a given time. Meter readers went around to the customer's quarters every week, took out the plates, and "weighed the bill."

Obviously, this was a poor makeshift. But it had to suffice till someone found a way to make instruments that read the product of volts, amperes, and time directly on a scale as watt hours. Meanwhile, electric companies charged flat rates for each light.

Siemens, Ayrton and Perry, Sir William Thomson and Deprez in Europe, and Weston in the United States were all working to produce an accurate, direct-reading meter. The Patent Office was crowded with applications showing ingenious variations of the old galvanometer principle. But D'Arsonval in France was the first to announce a really significant improvement, when in 1881 he patented an instrument design in which the magnetic elements were reversed. The usual method was to suspend an iron bar or compass needle at the center of a large stationary coil of wire. The French inventor used a fixed horseshoe magnet with a small rectangular coil of wire suspended between the poles, and free to turn. The taut wire by which the coil was supported brought current to and from the instrument. The application of this "dynamometer" principle to instruments was obviously a great advance, for the coil could be made featherlight and the magnet very strong. At the same time it was independent of the earth's field, insensitive to vibration, and inherently rugged and simple.

Weston, too, had hit upon the moving coil idea. According to his own testimony in subsequent lawsuits, he had been struggling with the measurement problem ever since he began dynamo-making in 1872, and had reached an understanding of the new principle long before D'Arsonval. Unfortunately, his habit of keeping his ideas jealously to himself until he was thoroughly ready to release them, lost him the priority. He did not announce his inventions in this category till 1884, thereby making certain of the usual tedious round of interferences and infringement suits. From the minute he did start work on instruments, D'Arsonval was his sworn rival, only less bitter an enemy than men like Edison and Brush, because he was so far removed.

Weston worked sporadically on the moving coil scheme for a voltmeter from 1882 on, giving it special thought only when his crude instruments annoyed him; making a burst of experiments, then dropping them for more pressing work. In 1884 he really put his mind to the problem, and almost immediately turned up important new material. "In the beginning of 1884," his assistant, Benecke, wrote in his notebook, "Mr. Weston made the first attempt to pivot the moving coil of an instrument, which was specially designed for the purpose of aiding in the adjustment of the Automatic Regulators used in conjunction with large incandescent lamps. The system was used at the Philadelphia Exhibition of the Franklin Institute in that year, for the adjustment of said regulators." This was the instrument already referred to. As Professor D. C. Jackson once said: "Dissatisfaction, not necessity, was the mother of Weston's invention."

The important advance was the use of pivots to hold the swinging coil, just as the movement of a watch is pivoted for frictionless turning. In abandoning the taut suspension wire used by D'Arsonval, Weston immediately lost the restoring effect given by the torsional twist of the wire, but was soon able to overcome it by adopting a coiled steel spring, again following watchmaking practice.

The poles of his magnet he fitted with curved "shoes," in much the same way that dynamo field pieces were tipped. This brought the magnetic flux equally close to the coil and made it uniform in all positions of swing. To enhance the effect still more, he added a central soft-iron core, fitting inside the coil but not touching it. This general arrangement was the basis of his first instrument patent.

One other advance of the greatest importance was added. D'Arsonval was winding his coils on a form, then making them rigid with cement and hanging them by themselves in the magnetic gap. Weston devised a thin, rectangular frame of copper (later changed to aluminum) and wound his coil on that. It gave a very solid support and, in addition, introduced something quite new—an automatic damping action. All delicately balanced instruments of the day would swing to and fro for a long time when placed in the circuit. The user had to wait patiently for them to stabilize by friction. Weston's copper support amounted to a single short-circuited turn of low resistance cutting the magnetic field. As it moved, eddy currents were induced which set up their own opposing field and so brought the coil to a standstill in the position dictated by the strength of the current to be measured.

The irony of it was that D'Arsonval had his name firmly attached to the moving coil arrangement; for years the moving coil instrument was known as the D'Arsonval type. It is even today.

5

Weston now had the prototype of the modern electrical measuring instrument in his grasp. It was 1885, and high time to commercialize the idea. But there were still serious hurdles in the way. The most serious—and scientists believed it insurmountable—was the fact that a permanent magnet, as then known, *did not stay permanent.* Gradually, over a long period, it weakened. This being the case, a reliable instrument was impossible because if the field strength changed, the coil and its pointer would take different positions for the same current flow.

Weston analyzed the situation and for a time agreed. He saw that the iron crystals oriented in one direction by the original magnetizing action gradually drifted back to a random arrangement and lost their combined force. The obvious answer was an artificial electromagnetic field whose strength could be held constant by adjustment.

This principle was satisfactory for a dynamo field, where a regulator could be used to control the generated voltage. But in an instrument intended as a reliable standard, such regulation would be a paradox. However, he decided to pursue the idea to its end.

Weston kept one assistant in charge of each line of investigation in the laboratory. His instrument man was George B. Prescott, Jr. Prescott was solidly against permanent magnets, and took up the artificial type with great zeal. With Weston closely following his work, he designed and built a compact little instrument that looked exactly like a miniature Weston dynamo. It had a rectangular frame with a pair of coils on each of the four legs and curved pole pieces in the middle. The coil was pivoted between these and carried a pointer that swept a scale arrangement along an arc of cardboard at one side. This was called a "potential indicator" and was intended to measure voltage.

Prescott immediately ran into trouble with variable magnetism. He found he could not maintain a field strength that was anywhere near constant, although he tried every kind of soft iron and all sorts of shapes. Weston thought that the problem might be solved by keeping the iron at its magnetic saturation point. But no iron alloy

Weston's "potential indicator"—forerunner of the voltmeter.

could be found that had an absolute value of saturation. The metal became nearly but not fully magnetized as excitation continued upward. Nearly was not good enough.

After Prescott had butted his head against the problem for many weeks, his employer said, one day, "Give it up, George. It won't work. It *can't work.*"

"Well, Mr. Weston," Prescott asserted, "it's got to work, or else we can't make satisfactory instruments. Permanent magnets are no good."

"Nevertheless we will go back to them," Weston decided. "A permanent magnet is right, scientifically. We simply do not know enough about it. We've got to find out."

"Then you admit defeat?"

"Nothing of the kind! Get back to permanent magnets, and let's see."

With great reluctance his assistant began investigating the "ageing" of magnet steel. He was soon ready to eat his hasty words.

A close analysis of the impermanence of permanent magnets presently revealed the probable cause. An actual flow of flux around the magnetic circuit seemed to be necessary to keep the crystals properly oriented. If this circuit was broken, the magnetic forces took shortcut paths and tended to weaken themselves. So long as a soft-iron bar or "keeper" was placed across the pole ends, the flux flowed smoothly and kept to its proper path. But when the keeper was removed, each pole began to influence the crystal alignment at the knee of the magnet and break it up. This action continued very slowly till a steady state was reached—perhaps after many years.

Weston's answer to this was twofold: Build the instrument to have the very smallest air gaps possible and find some way to produce premature ageing in the magnet steel, so that it would have settled down before use began. He set Prescott to work in the chemical laboratory, testing every available type of steel for its magnetic properties. He himself went on to other research.

6

The work on Tamidine had attracted a great deal of attention in the chemical industry, especially because of Weston's great knowledge of cellulose. He had recently been asked by his old friends, Hanson and Van Winkle, to develop a pyroxylin varnish or lacquer that would dry fast and present a very hard surface. Feeling that he must do the job at once, he set to work and drove ahead steadily for three months, putting everything else aside. At the end of that time the formula was ready and was immediately sold to the customer. The inventor had proved to himself, if he still needed proof, that he could proceed in his own establishment with difficult problems and solve them profitably.

Weston patented the lacquer formula, of course, and it antedated by many years any other disclosure of the kind. There is a story that, some thirty years later, when General Motors scientists sought protection for their first automobile lacquer, they were informed by their attorneys that the idea was not patentable. A search had showed that Weston's patent had covered the field so broadly that lacquers had been in the public domain ever since its expiration.

In the fall of '86 Weston was ready to go back to electrical instruments. By this time the laboratory was finished and ready to concentrate all its facilities on this important problem.

Prescott, meanwhile, had thoroughly investigated steels and was ready to specify the best magnetic alloy. "But it still shows ageing," he warned. "You'll never get away from that."

"Then we'll accept it and use it," Weston retorted. "I have an idea for speeding up the ageing and getting it out of the way."

The scheme was as ingenious as anything he had ever devised. First, the steel was properly shaped and then stabilized by very careful heating and cooling, so that no strains were left to mar the smoothness of the magnetic circuit. Then it was aged many thousand times as fast as nature could do it by contact with the poles of a specially designed electromagnet in which the flux could be reversed. With this the steel was repeatedly magnetized in one direction and then the other, until the many reversals had completely oriented the crystals in a single direction, regimenting them like an army of obedient soldiers.

The final step was the permanent magnetizing of the material up to a strength no more than two-thirds of its saturation point. Weston reasoned that at this low value there would be very little tendency for the magnetism to decay, even over a long period of time.

With these three factors—ageing, low saturation, and a carefully designed closed magnetic circuit—Weston had solved the problem of the constant magnetic field for instrument use.

It is difficult to decide whether the magnetic ageing of the steel or the reduction of the leakage gap was the greater contribution.

The latter was certainly the more obvious fundamental. Kelvin, Ayrton, and D'Arsonval were all using magnets with large gaps, and accepted the fact that their instruments had to be recalibrated continually, which made them useless in nontechnical hands. It is certain that ageing alone would not have solved the problem. The closed magnetic circuit was essential. Modern instruments, indeed, are designed with gaps about 5/100ths of an inch wide, all of them recognizing Weston's basic discovery.

From the completion of the first experimental instrument, Weston knew that he had solved the principal problems. In December, 1886, Prescott finished the pioneer model—a voltmeter—the first truly portable instrument ever made. Without further delay he called in Quimby and they wrote up a patent on it. This was granted on November 6, 1888. On that patent rested the company which he was soon to form, and to which his real fame is due.

Regardless of Weston's pioneer work, the Europeans were loath to give him the credit, even after his products had flooded the world. As late as 1892 the *Journal of the Institution of Electrical Engineers* in London damned him with faint praise:

There is one species of D'Arsonval galvanometer which does not hail from France, nor is it an English copy of French instruments. It is made in America. We always assume that Americans cannot make instruments, and that may be true generally; but there is certainly one American who can, and that is Mr. Weston. His voltmeters are only D'Arsonval galvanometers in which the current is led in by two hairsprings, which also act as the controlling force.

This was a considerable understatement. Weston's instrument contained many more improvements on the D'Arsonval principle than are here credited.

But Europe was indeed difficult to win over. As soon as the new instrument company had been started, Weston sent one of his stock voltmeters to Germany to the Deutsche Physicalische Reichsanstalt, then the only standardizing laboratory in the world. The Germans were exceedingly skeptical of the magnetic permanence which he claimed, and refused to give the instrument a certificate until they had tested it continuously for five years. At the end of that time it was as accurate as ever; with considerable admiration they gave Weston their full endorsement.

Nowadays, meters are frequently returned to the factory after twenty-five years of steady use and show no measurable weakening of the magnets.

By the end of 1886 Weston had been granted four patents on electrical instruments, embodying practically every step in the development, from the delicate galvanometer type to the final dynamometer principle. This included an integrating current meter—what we should call a watt-hour meter—and several forms of mercury device, indicating current by the amount of mercury transferred from one portion of the apparatus to another. He had not, however, entered his claims for protection on the compact new instrument which had reached a workable state in December, 1886. His mind was already off on a tangent.

This is only explainable by the fact that he moved so rapidly from one matter to another that he failed to consider the practical importance of early protection. He believed he was so far ahead of his competitors that he could afford a delay. He may also have felt that to support the heavy expenses of his private laboratory, he had better get out and earn some money. At any rate, with the coming of 1887, he plunged himself and his entire staff into the business of furnishing expert witness service to various concerns who were anxious to hire him. The new electrical instruments had to wait.

Weston was in no danger of starvation, for he entered into agreements with several firms for acting as an expert court witness at an annual retainer of $5,000 or thereabouts. This was by no means a one-man job. It devolved upon him to furnish the technical background for the inventions he was defending for others, and soon the entire laboratory was busy making elaborate models of machines, principles and details of early inventions. He had a genius for demonstration, and under his guidance many ingenious wood models of dynamos, arc-lamp mechanisms, and incandescent-lamp components were turned out. Weston abundantly earned his salaries, because in those days the patent cases were being tried before judges who knew next to nothing about the technical aspects of electricity.

His great clarity and logic, coupled with the exhibition of the models helped the jurists to render favorable decisions for his side.

In this model work, one of his assistants, H. F. Nehr, was the principal genius, an instrument maker of great skill who had been with him since 1880. Nehr was intensely loyal, too. One day in the summer of 1887, Weston rushed into the shop, got hold of Nehr and started him working on a model of an electric traction motor which was needed in court. Nehr got busy at four o'clock in the morning and worked 43 hours without stopping, in order to get the job finished. In the midst of it, the main steam engine in the laboratory went out of whack, and everybody had to drop what he was doing and help repair it.

Things went on like this till the fall of '87, when Edward Quimby wrote to him, scolding him for letting the instrument matter languish. He pointed out that everybody else was working on electrical instruments, too, and that a patent was absolutely essential, immediately. The instrument, Quimby thought, had great commercial value and should be pushed with all possible haste.

Weston, for once, listened to him, and the laboratory was switched back to instruments as suddenly as it had been taken off them.

There were still a few matters that needed to be solved. One was the problem of the spiral springs supporting the moving coil. The only springs obtainable were, of course, made of steel, and this interfered with the proper stability of the magnetic circuit. They also offered too high a resistance to the currents flowing in and out of the coil. Everyone else who was attempting instrument making was using steel springs, thinking that nothing else was possible. Weston rejected the idea and started his metallurgical department on a search for a nonmagnetic material that would have the resilience of steel but a much better conductivity. After considerable research, this was found in a special low-resistance alloy for millivoltmeters and a phosphor-bronze alloy for other instruments. Nothing else has been used in ordinary instruments since, though beryllium-copper has recently come into the field for special purposes.

Another problem in materials was posed by the pointer to be

carried by the coil as it swung around. Weston decided that a thin aluminum rod would be best. But in those days aluminum could not be drawn into wire fine enough for this purpose. He solved the difficulty by developing a special alloy of aluminum which was so ductile that small-diameter wire of high uniformity could be made. Satisfactory pointers were turned out with this. Later, he found that he could draw exceedingly fine tubing with the alloy, and this quickly replaced solid wire. Weston now had a stiff, almost weightless pointer.

But the weight, although small, had to be balanced. The answer to this was a small metal quadrant fixed opposite to the pointer, carrying a rim with threaded holes in which small screws could be adjusted in and out. Perfect balance could thus be assured. In later designs a balance cross was substituted for the quadrant.

Weston's pointer arrangement has come down through the art virtually intact. In the late war, when instruments in ships and planes had to withstand explosive shocks, pointers were made so strong that they could withstand an acceleration of 1500-G—that is, they could support 1500 times their own weight without bending out of shape. In fact, the whole structure had to meet this requirement. A modern military instrument could be dropped on a concrete floor without putting it out of business.

## 7

A far more important problem than the pointer, which led to one of Weston's most important inventions in the instrument field, was the "shunt."

It was well understood that when a current passed through a resistance a voltage drop occurred, according to Ohm's law. The idea soon struck him that all electrical measuring instruments could be constructed as voltmeters if a secondary circuit were arranged in parallel to the moving coil. When an ammeter was to be built, it was only necessary to give this parallel circuit a low but appreciable resistance and then measure the drop across it. Such a circuit in general was called a "shunt," following British engineering practice, which had borrowed the term used to describe a railroad siding.

In other words, the current would divide between the two circuits

in inverse proportion to their resistance values. If the coil had a
very high resistance in proportion to the shunt, only a minute current would flow in it. But this would still serve as an accurate measure of the much larger main current. The instrument scale could
then be calibrated directly in amperes.

The only material available for producing a measurable resistance
drop in a short length of conductor was German silver. But this he
soon found to be unsatisfactory because of its large temperature
coefficient. As current flowed through it, it heated, and like all other
metals, its resistance increased with temperature. A shunt would be
no good if its resistance changed, unless all measurements could be
related to temperature. To measure this as a condition to making
electrical measurements was not desirable.

The electrical profession at that time labored under a misconcep-
tion quite as foolish as the contention that the electric light could
not be "subdivided." This was the definition of a metal—a substance whose resistance increased with temperature. Conversely, a
nonmetal was defined as one whose resistance *went down* with rising
temperature. Carbon, a nonmetal, was considered an excellent example of this rule.

Weston realized that there was something wrong with the defini-
tions and decided to improve upon them. It should be possible, he
thought, to make a metallic alloy with a negligible temperature
coefficient, or even a negative one. At least, he hoped to discover
one whose resistance remained reasonably constant for ordinary
working temperatures. If this could be done, his shunt instrument
would be practical.

He began experimenting immediately with commercial German
silver, an alloy of copper, nickel, and zinc, but found that there was
little consistency in its behavior, since every slight variation in its
proportions greatly changed its electrical properties. The alloy was
all imported from Germany, so that there was no simple way to
control the manufacture. So he undertook to make new alloys of
his own. Very soon he had devised a formula which contained some
30 per cent nickel and which gave a resistance of almost twice that
of German silver, together with a much smaller temperature coefficient. This was known as "Alloy No. 1."

The alloy was not suitable for shunts, still having a variable resistance. But it was highly encouraging as a start in the right direction. Weston now set his laboratory men to work on a systematic search for the right alloy. More than three hundred were compounded, while the inventor himself supervised every experiment, even to the final drawing of the wire. The final result was an alloy of nickel and copper which actually had a small *negative* coefficient. With this, for the time being, he decided to be satisfied. He called it his "Alloy No. 2."

But Weston was not satisfied long. These early metallurgical researches were only the beginning of a struggle that he kept up for many years. "The very best German silver we could make," he admitted later, "was not good enough for instrument work, nor was it good enough for standard. It had to be used with great care, and you had to be very careful about measurements. You can scarcely imagine what that means in a laboratory where thousands of electrical measurements are made in a day."

Nevertheless, it was not wise to delay the completion of the first commercial instrument because of imperfect shunts. So he decided to go ahead with what he had. Unfortunately, American wire mills were unable to draw the new alloy into wire fine enough for Weston, and he was forced to send the specifications abroad and have the work done in Germany. There it was renamed "Constantan" and soon became so popular that everybody began using it. Presently the electrical profession got the impression that the Germans had *invented* it.

In the spring of 1888, Weston applied for a basic patent on the moving-coil voltmeter, and the patent was issued on November 6th of that year. In this very long and involved specification, the entire arrangement of the modern direct-current instrument is set forth— the permanent magnet, pivoted coil, the damping frame of copper, the curved pole pieces, the spiral springs, and, lastly, a simple arrangement for incorporating several shunt coils so that the instrument, by the shifting of a plug, could be given various voltage ranges or used as an ammeter for currents up to 150 amperes.

This first commercially practical instrument was actually a millivoltmeter, and several designs were built in the early part of 1888

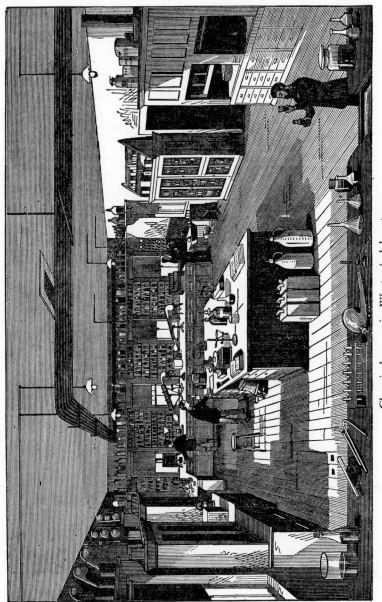

Chemical room in Weston's laboratory.

in order to drive out the worst of the "bugs" that were bound to be present while an experimental model was being refined into a production unit.

The third version of this instrument was taken in hand by Weston's good friend, Professor E. A. Colby, who was anxious to see how it behaved in service. In the next few months he visited electrical laboratories in many eastern universities and also a number of testing rooms belonging to Weston's competitors, where he compared the instrument with the very best galvanometers in America. "The result of Mr. Colby's use of this instrument," Weston testified later, in a lawsuit arising from its patent, "was to show that its accuracy was greater than the laboratory standards ordinarily employed and that it could be used extremely roughly without injury or deterioration. A careful test showed that the magnetic field remained permanent."

Weston was confident, that spring, that he had the best instrument so far made. The question was what to do with it to make it a profitable commercial proposition.

8

Instruments at that time were principally important for laboratory use, and there would undoubtedly be a good market for them. But the large demand for measuring instruments was bound to come from the mushrooming electric power and light business, totally unequipped with efficient means of rapid measurement. Voltmeters here would be useful in maintaining the quality of the service— lights burned well or poorly according to the steadiness of the circuit potential. The real need, however, was for an ampere-measuring instrument to determine the *quantity* of the service, and hence the revenue. The crude apparatus for measuring load required massive equipment and elaborate calculations, even for the simplest readings. The field for ammeters was wide open.

Weston knew well enough that he would not be able to meet this demand immediately—not until he had devised a high-capacity shunt that would be virtually free of temperature coefficient trouble. Nevertheless, he decided to make a beginning. In this he was strongly urged on by the Quimbys, father and son, who insisted that no time was to be lost. It was important to start up a new manufacturing concern at once, they insisted. Weston would have liked to be in a position to put up the money and make a start with full control in his own hands. But this he could not do, even though his own premises were used for the factory. The laboratory had taken most of the extra money he had earned from his witness fees. There was nothing to start a business with.

The Quimbys loyally offered to come forward with some cash themselves, and one of them suggested a third investor who might be willing to participate. This was Franz O. Matthiessen, who owned a sugar refinery in Jersey City and who had purchased a number of arc lamps from Weston some years before. Matthiessen was a very different sort from the United States Company's people. A self-made man and an immigrant like Weston, he knew the value of hard work, particularly at the beginning of a new enterprise. With very little persuasion he agreed to come in, with considerable money.

On March 31, 1888, the partnership was officially formed. One thousand shares of stock were solemnly issued and distributed among the four partners, at a book value of $100 apiece. Weston received 580 shares in return for his patents on electrical instruments, and for the use of his laboratory as a temporary starting point for the venture. The Weston Electrical Instrument Company was chartered in New Jersey in April of the same year.

"Thus was Weston's fourth and last company born," says a company booklet, issued fifty years later. "Like the three which preceded it—his nickel plating business, his dynamo business and his arc light business—this company was concerned with making, improving and selling a new kind of electrical apparatus. But in one very important respect it was different from the other three. For this time Edward Weston had started in a business that had to deal with the whole field of electricity and not just one corner of it. His problems from now on were not confined to dynamos or lights or electrolysis; he had to follow every electrical improvement that came along and find some way to measure it efficiently. That is the chief significance behind the founding of the Weston Electrical Instrument Company in 1888. It meant that the 38-year-old inventor had finally reached the life he was looking for, a life spent in constantly devising and discovering new mechanisms that satisfied him scientifically."

This is a significant comment. Weston had taken on what is perhaps the most difficult road to prominence in any field of endeavor: a work which brings a man and his achievements to the test in every phase of an art, rather than by merely developing a single item and perfecting it; what might be called the horizontal rather than the vertical approach. He succeeded so well that Weston instruments have been the unqualified leaders ever since, both in the United States and abroad.

Manufacturing was begun with a small staff immediately, the product being simply the millivoltmeter already described, with Constantan shunts to transform it into an ammeter. For the next five years Weston put his time almost exclusively on instruments, and took out a constant stream of patents which, taken together, cover almost the whole history of early instrument development. Save for a momentary digression to write a patent on the utilization of solar energy for generating electricity, he did not depart from instrument work at all. And this interesting digression was, in fact, an offshoot of his instrument work.

The alloy Constantan, which he had invented, served extremely well as a low-coefficient material for instrument shunts. But it had one serious drawback. At the points where the shunts were connected to the copper or brass terminals of the instrument, any change in temperature would generate "parasitic" currents—another way of describing the action of a thermocouple composed of dissimilar metals. These currents, or potentials, upset the steady action of the Constantan itself and produced almost as bad an effect as though the shunts were made of the highly variable German silver.

The solar energy patent described a blackened thermocouple coil placed in the path of rays from a lens or mirror. Currents generated by the heat were passed into a storage battery and there accumulated for later use. Weston never built such a device; if he had, he would have found that it gave too small an amount of energy to be useful. But it is interesting to note that one of the most modern of suggestions for the transformation of heat units in fuel into mechanical energy contemplates a bank of highly sensitive thermocouples exposed to the radiant energy of rapidly burning fuel, thus producing electrical energy direct.

This problem of thermoelectrical action at the junctions of the shunts was so serious that it kept Weston busy for several years and made it nearly impossible to produce a reliable ammeter suitable for large currents. In the meantime, he ran into another difficulty in the form of the heating of the moving coil itself. As the temperature of this coil rose, its resistance increased about 2/10 of 1 per cent for every degree Fahrenheit, and the readings were considerably thrown off. He spent a great deal of time devising and patenting methods of combating the trouble. In one of these schemes he ingeniously included a thermometer, bent in an arc parallel to the arc of the scale. The bulb of the thermometer was placed close to the coil, and the indication of temperature was in plain sight as one began reading the instrument. A small rheostat was built into the base connected in series with the moving coil. Its handle passed over a scale calibrated in degrees. One need only observe the temperature, then move the rheostat to the proper position to compensate for the heating effect in the coil.

After the first voltmeter design was stabilized, the new company rapidly began expanding its line of instruments. Voltmeters up to five or six thousand volts were easily made, and these were followed shortly by ammeters of fairly high capacity. Then Weston began patenting alternating-current instruments of like capacity. They were very nearly the same in general design, except that the permanent magnet was replaced by a stationary coil connected in series with the moving coil.

The little factory-within-a-laboratory was a great success. From the very beginning, Weston instruments were accepted as the best that could be made. There was never any difficulty about obtaining customers. The inventor was known to be a stickler for accuracy and excellence in everything he designed and built. No one questioned his supremacy. His competitors never reached an equal footing.

The market for the new instruments immediately broadened to include every phase of the industry. But the most important demand in the early days came from laboratories. Here at last was a portable instrument that could take the place of the cumbersome tangent galvanometer. College engineering departments hastened to provide themselves with Weston voltmeters and ammeters. Within a short time, hearing that such reliable results were possible with the new instruments, competing instrument makers began to buy them for use in calibrating their own products. Ironically, Weston was helping others to raise their standards toward the level of his own.

So, he went on to design even more perfect instruments. The patents of these first years cover continual small improvements: better balance, better ways of winding the coils, better materials, better pivots, better appearance. Meanwhile, recognizing the fact that the tangent galvanometer was still the most sensitive means of standardizing electric currents, he designed and built a few instruments of that type for his own use in manufacturing his regular line of instruments.

He had reached a goal that few inventors in history have ever reached. He had become a criterion in a great new art, a standard of reference for everybody else. Although his competitors made and sold instruments for as little as one-third of his own prices, he still sold more than they did. So good was his product that he sealed each instrument when it was made, guaranteeing its accuracy as long as nobody broke the seals and tampered with the mechanism.

In a symbolic way he had sealed his supremacy beyond reach of his competitors. All over the world his name became synonymous with top quality. "It is particularly noticeable in all of the technical schools in Germany," said a contemporary journal, "that the electrical equipments are decidedly German. Scarcely an instrument, dynamo or motor of foreign make . . . can be found in any of the laboratories, with the exception of Weston ammeters and voltmeters."

A reporter from the *Electrical World,* visiting the laboratory in 1890 wrote: "The Weston Electrical Instrument Company, under the supervision of Mr. Edward Weston, the celebrated electrician, have had such a big run on their new voltmeters that they have had to make special arrangements for their production in large quantities."

The special provisions were the establishment of a new factory.

Two years in the laboratory had completely swamped its space and machinery. The new plant was a four-story building on William Street, and here at last there was room for everything. Every standard tool and machine for doing delicate work was installed, and Weston

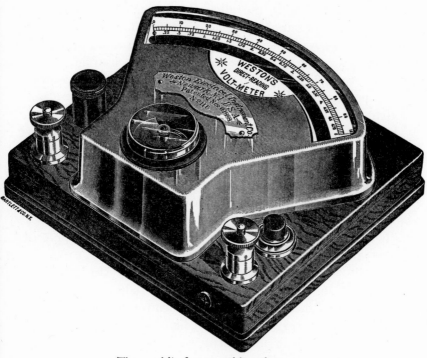

The world's first portable voltmeter.

and his growing corps of assistants were diligently at work designing and building many more that were highly specialized for the work in hand.

That factory was the beginning of an industry, and the lead it achieved then has never been lost in the half century that has passed since.

9

Having captured the top position in the laboratory instrument field, Weston next tackled the much larger market in the growing power industry. By this time practically every city and town in the country had its own electric light system. The demand for a good method of measuring ampere load was urgent. No one had been able to devise a reliable ammeter. His own, good as it was, could not cope with the now huge currents that were everyday practice.

Ever since inventing the alloy Constantan, Weston had been worried about the variable resistance of the shunt ammeter. In the laboratory this was not serious, since provision could be made for temperature readings and the interpretaion of instrument indications by formula. But in power stations this was impossible. A simple pointer had to indicate the current values and these had to be right.

Instruments then in use had two soft-iron cores, wound with wire and placed so as to repel each other with a force proportional to the current. It was a crude scheme, and involved large errors. The indicators—they could not be dignified by the term instruments— were so bulky that they could not be installed on a switchboard; their scales were not evenly divided; their pointers swung back and forth interminably before settling down; they used up appreciable current in heat; they were expensive.

Actually, one ammeter designed for Edison by Lord Kelvin was as large as an office desk. J. Van Vleck, Edison's chief station engineer, stated in 1890 that no conveniently small instrument was possible. Of all the experts consulted, here and abroad, only Weston told him that a shunt instrument would solve the problem. Van Vleck said that was impossible, too.

Weston knew that if he could overcome the single difficulty of the shunt, he would have a clear field for his highly accurate, compact moving-coil type of instrument. Four years after Van Vleck's statement, he had overcome it, and Van Vleck himself was installing long rows of Weston ammeters, capable of reading as high as 7,000 amperes. By 1895 the company stated: "We are prepared to make ammeters of any capacity up to 100,000 amperes."

The researches that resulted in a successful shunt instrument were begun by Weston in his laboratory even before the company itself was started, and were, indeed, a part of his general investigations into special alloys. But it took full five years to reach success. As we have seen, he began his intensive search for a shunt metal by experimenting with German silver, and eventually developed "Constantan." This had a reasonably small rise of resistance with temperature, but was troublesome because of thermoelectric action. But in the course of further experiments Weston tried adding a little manganese to the copper and nickel, and immediately got better results. The first improvement resulted in alloys having a specific resistance (per unit volume) about three times as high as German silver—sixty times that of copper. But it was found subsequently that the best material had about half these ratios.

A very high specific resistance was an essential for good shunts, because it would permit large cross sections to be used with a small length of conductor, and still provide the appreciable voltage drop required to operate the instrument.

With this encouraging beginning, Weston drove ahead, spending long hours over his chemical bench, trying first one proportion, then another, fusing the new alloy and shaping it into wire, then making careful test runs at many different temperatures. Almost at once he noted that the second vital requirement had been met—a very low temperature coefficient. Early samples of the alloy showed even less resistance change than Constantan. It was only a question, he felt, of keeping on till he found what he was after: a metal whose temperature coefficient was negligible.

Supervising and inspiring thousands of experiments and tests, Weston gradually approached this goal. Other work intervened; the instrument company was formed, prospered and finally moved into its own plant. Still the alloy investigation continued. Then Weston finally produced a metal that actually had a negative temperature coefficient: its resistance went down as it grew hotter. This was the achievement he had been trying for; it was only a short additional step to work backwards from a negative to a negligible dependence upon temperature.

He had done what physics books said was impossible, and with it had broken down the accepted distinction between a metal and a nonmetal.

It had not been a simple proposition. These remarkable results were not obtained merely by trying one thing after another, but by reasoning out the probable influence of each phase of the compounding of the alloy. An essential step was an exact method for pretreating the metal before use. Weston showed that the alloy by itself fell short of the desired characteristics. Only when it was carefully heat-treated did it produce results. The treatment itself proved to be quite as important as the exact composition of the alloy.

## 10

In 1892 Weston had finally completed his discovery—an alloy of copper, nickel, and manganese prepared by a complicated series of heat-treatments. In May, 1893, he received a basic patent on the composition, manufacture, and use of the material for electrical resistors. The first use of the alloy was in the series resistance coils in Weston voltmeters. For the first time, such instruments could be built that were free of inaccuracies caused by temperature. It was one of Weston's greatest contributions to the electrical art. Out of three metals whose possible combinations were practically infinite, he had made an alloy which would change the standards of precision in electrical measurement. He had done this in the face of the solid opposition of thought of the scientific world.

Samples of the new zero-temperature-coefficient metal soon reached the Reichsanstalt in Germany, and its scientists accepted it eagerly and began to make studies of their own. Presently they had standardized its proportions to definite percentages of each metal, and had given it the name Manganin. But they were careful to credit Weston with the discovery. In the eyes of the rest of the world, however, he was not so fortunate. He had driven the research through with his rare gift of concentration, practically immuring himself from the outside world while he did it. This insistence on secrecy prevented him from receiving the acclaim that was due him. It was the Germans, not Weston, who got the credit for Manganin.

In 1892 Lord Kelvin addressed the British Association for the Advancement of Science. He was then the world's most famous electrical physicist. He was taking his countrymen to task for having no national standardization laboratory such as the German Reichsanstalt. Professor von Helmholtz had just preceded him in lauding the organization. "One thing Professor von Helmholtz did not mention," said Kelvin, "was the discovery by the Anstalt of a metal whose temperature coefficient with respect to electrical resistance is practically nil. This is just what we have been waiting for for twenty or thirty years. . . . The Physicalische Anstalt had not been in existence two years before this valuable metal was discovered."

Professor von Helmholtz rose quickly. "The discovery of a metal whose resistance diminishes with temperature was made by an American engineer," he said succinctly.

Ayrton was on his feet too. "By an Englishman—Weston," he corrected.

Kelvin made an adroit escape from his predicament. "That serves but to intensify the position I wish to take," he suavely observed. "Whether the discovery was made by an Anglo-American, an American Englishman, or an Englishman in America, it is not gratifying to national pride to know that these discoveries were not made in this country."

Thus Weston's name upon this great forward step was inadvertently blurred by the work of the German laboratories. The Germans could not be blamed for this, however. In fact, the German rolling mill, Isabellenhuette, that had first made Manganin to the Anstalt's specifications had coined the name "Westonin" for it. Later "Manganin" seemed simpler and more descriptive, and was adopted instead.

Credit or not, Weston's alloy rapidly swept the world. Eventually, instrument makers everywhere were using it for shunts and resistors. Nothing else could equal it even remotely.

II

But in 1893, with the first basic patent on his desk, all this was in the future. The immediate problem was to tackle the great new field of electric-power instrumentation, which meant the design of central-station ammeters.

There was no important change to be made in the instrument mechanism. The problem was to introduce the resistive shunt material and to *dissipate the heat* generated in it. Weston felt that it

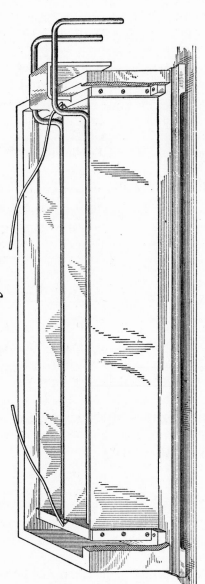

*Fig: 1*

Model of the 400 Ampere Franklin Institute Shunt, omitting its Oil Bath
and Mercury Terminal.

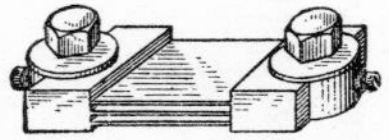

*Fig: 3*

400 Ampere Weston Shunt having the same drop of potential,
and employing same german silver as the F. J. Shunt.

*Fig: 2*

400 Ampere Weston Shunt

Weston shunts compared with oil-cooled shunt of the same capacity.

was important to hold the temperature down as much as possible, to avoid variations in the resistance and to prevent damage to the material. Therefore, he tackled the design from the viewpoint of the most efficient means of heat dissipation. The simplest arrangement, and the one he used first, was to provide the shunt circuit resistor material with massive terminal blocks, large in volume compared to the shunt itself. The heat quickly flowed to these and was radiated away.

This may not sound like a great invention, but it caused much stir in scientific circles. Nobody else, either in America or Europe, seems to have thought of the idea of dissipating shunt heat through the terminals.

A word should be said about the loss of energy sustained in the shunt. Though the temperature rise was considerable, the loss in watts was nearly negligible. Weston quotes an example in an article in *Electrical Engineering* in 1894:

This [competing] ammeter was a good deal better than the average, so far as efficiency is concerned. It was a 600-ampere instrument, and in the conductor there was a loss of 21 watts. That looks rather small . . . it amounts to a quarter of one cent per hour—six cents a day and a little over $22 a year. But if you have ten of them that means $222. But the meter had joints and these were not well fitted, and there was a further loss there. . . . To use that ammeter would require and average of ten feet of conductor to carry the current to and from it. In this there would be a loss of 64.2 watts. The instrument and conductor together would represent $89 waste of energy on the basis stated. Now, you can eliminate [these losses] if you use a shunt type of instrument properly designed, . . . the instrument which consumed 18 watts now consumes only .0021 of a watt, and instead of costing $18 a year to run it costs you 0.22 of a cent.

In one instance, in a railway power station, an instrument loss of $459.64 per year was reduced to a few cents when Weston ammeters replaced the older instruments.

It was not surprising that the Weston Instrument Company was swamped with business. Again his inventions had become a world standard. The station ammeter of the shunt type really put the company on the map. Ten years later, the statement was made in the shunt litigation that "hardly a single station ampere meter can be found on the switchboard of any direct-current central station or isolated plant either in this country or abroad, in which there is not made use of the shunt described in [Weston's] patent."

If he had needed it, Weston could not have had a more fortunate "break" than the Columbian Exposition of 1893 in Chicago. At the suggestion of Professor Ayrton, who had come over with Kelvin from England to sit on the committee judging electrical apparatus, Weston instruments were adopted exclusively for the making of tests on the various dynamos and lamps that were shown. Weston had received the highest honor which it was possible for his colleagues to give him.

Among the prominent technical men at the Exposition was Dugald C. Jackson, then an electric traction engineer and later Professor of Electrical Engineering at M.I.T. Jackson was on the Jury of Awards, which held numerous meetings in the evenings, before which the various inventors appeared to discuss their work. When Weston's turn came, he launched into a detailed description and explanation of his many inventions. "When he told us about his shunt instruments," said Jackson, "the Europeans among us just did not believe it could be done; they had to be shown. But it was done. And we were all much impressed when Weston explained his empirical formula for calculating the saturation and other data in magnetic circuits for generators and motors. John Hopkinson in England later worked out a theoretical approach to this same problem. His findings corroborated Weston in nearly every detail.

"Weston was so successful because he was mechanically expert. He knew how to do things well."

This tribute and many others implied in the soaring demand for his instruments gave Weston great confidence. As one expression of it he offered to replace the cumbersome and wasteful measuring devices in the great Edison Duane Street Station in New York with his own instruments and take in payment only one-half of one year's savings. The proposition was not accepted. But Weston instruments completely supplanted the old, and solved the heavy problems of losses in measurement.

12

Now that the moving-coil type of voltmeter and ammeter had become standardized in the power stations of the world, new problems began to plague the inventor. Weston's instruments were famous for their accuracy, which came from the extreme sensitivity of the magnetic circuit and the rotating element. But in spite of the fact that he had done everything possible to close the magnet around coil and core and thus confine the circuit to the instrument, it remained sensitive to outside magnetic fields. As soon as Weston station meters began to spread about the country, complaints arose that they were seriously affected by stray fields.

At first Weston was angered by this, and stated categorically that his instruments could not indicate incorrectly. But presently he had to retreat from that position and do something about the problem.

A paper presented before the Franklin Institute by J. A. Stewart, a Philadelphia engineer, gave much interesting data on stray fields. He had found that a common file placed near a Weston voltmeter would produce an error in readings. A bench vise near by would do the same thing. If two voltmeters were placed side by side, they might throw each other out, or not, depending on their positions. Another engineer, commenting on the paper, said that a Philadelphia power station had tried to use moving-coil voltmeters on a switchboard behind which a bus bar was carrying heavy currents. The instruments were entirely unreliable. It was his guess that meters could not be installed on switchboards at all, but must be placed in some special location remote from magnetic fields.

Still another complaint emanated from the Imperial Bureau of Standards in Vienna, and covered not only Weston's but all European instruments. The Bureau stated that, "among many other things," merely to rub the glass over the instrument dial with a clean dry cloth would put such a charge on it as to introduce a large error in pointer readings. This would not happen on a rainy day. Perhaps one should not attempt to use precision instruments except in bad weather!

Finally there came a reminder from closer to home. D. C. Jackson, then in charge of the Cleveland street railway powerhouse, wrote Weston that his instruments, installed on the main switchboard, were not giving reliable service. He suggested that the stray field from the dynamos might be causing the trouble. "Dr. Weston replied in his customary positive manner," says Jackson, "stating that this 'just could not be so'; that Weston meters were always accurate.

"However, Dr. Weston's statement did not correct the inaccuracies and after several more exchanges of correspondence he was induced to make a special trip to Cleveland to show the men how to use his meters."

What he found when he strode grimly into the station, was that a battery of venerable Edison dynamos was being used, in close proximity to the instruments. These machines had smooth drum armatures with the windings placed outside the metal instead of in slots, as Weston had his. Under heavy load the dynamos filled the vicinity with a powerful stray field that upset the magnetic conditions of every device within range, meters included.

Although Weston had long since conceived an enduring dislike of Edison and a certain contempt for his engineering designs, he recognized that this time he himself was wrong. Characteristically, he took one look at the situation, admitted his error to Jackson, and caught the first train back to Newark to remedy the trouble.

The problem of keeping stray magnetic fields away from a delicate instrument was not simple. Shielding must be used, but it must not influence the shape of the field within the instrument itself. But it was the sort of difficulty Weston liked to solve. He did solve it, though not until he had tried many types and methods of shielding.

Generally, the scheme was to analyze the magnetic circuit of the instrument and determine its vulnerable points. These appeared at first to be only in the region of the pole pieces and coil. But by testing with a strong external magnet, Weston discovered that stray lines of force from almost any direction would cause trouble. Shielding of the entire instrument would be required. Beginning with a soft-iron cover to enclose the whole thing, he added more and more metal until every part was heavily iron-clad. The practical difficulties of doing this were considerable, and Weston hated to see his originally beautiful design buried in iron. But it had to be done. It was many years before gradual refinement eliminated the clumsiness and gave us the compact, streamlined instruments we have today. But it was Weston's habit of frontal attack on a situation the moment he discovered it, that saved the moving-coil instrument from failure in the important power field.

## 13

So far we have dealt wholly with Weston's direct-current instruments. However, he was not unmindful of the rising importance of alternating-current power. While he was making his start as the world's leading authority on electrical measurements in 1888, the spectacular "Battle of the Currents" was joined. Edison, far in the lead as a central-station builder, had covered the country with direct-current systems. Opposite him were arrayed a number of important competitors: Westinghouse, Stanley, Thomson—all of whom were scrambling to perfect an alternating-current system of generators, transformers, motors, and switchgear that could oust Edison from his supremacy by destroying the "three-mile limit." Direct current could not be distributed at operating voltage for more than three miles without prohibitive loss. Alternating-current power could be transmitted economically at high voltage for many miles, as Stanley had shown. The Edison companies, however, were not disposed to admit that the limitation was serious. They proposed to keep electric power decentralized, with generating stations close to their loads everywhere.

The controversy became extremely virulent, in the fashion of those days. Libelous booklets were distributed by both sides, magnifying the dangers of the opposition system. In a pamphlet bound in scarlet covers and titled "A Warning from the Edison Electric Light Company," every competitor in the field was pilloried, and with them the a-c system itself. "It is clear," asserted the direct-current champions, "that high pressure, particularly if accompanied by rapid alternations, is not destined to assume any permanent position. It would be legislated out of existence in a very brief period even if it did not previously die a natural death."

And a great deal more besides. But the march of alternating current was not stopped. Edison well knew that it could not be. It was the logical method of distributing electricity.

From 1890 onward, electrical engineers constantly urged Weston to invent an a-c meter that was as accurate and as portable as his d-c instruments. He needed little urging. He had seen the demand coming for some time and had been considering the new problems. About 1889 he had begun to build prototypes and apply for patents on fundamental principles. He was of course not alone in this. The Westinghouse people, and particularly Elihu Thomson, were deeply immersed in a-c design. It was to be a race from the start.

Weston's primary aim was to utilize the essentials of the instrument already existing, and to develop an interchangeable meter that would work equally well on a-c and d-c. His contemporaries thought he was crazy, but he proved otherwise. Not, however, until a multitude of harassing problems had been solved. The main stumbling block was that in alternating-current work the self-inductance of even a small coil of wire might be so great as to produce enormous errors. The coil set up an opposing magnetic field of its own, which definitely limited the current that could pass. Other inventors who had tried to ignore this effect had been unable to build voltmeters that were of any value at all. The use of soft-iron cores, as then designed, introduced eddy currents and upset the linear relationship, and of course permanent magnets could not be used at all.

Weston swept all obstacles quickly aside. Instead of the permanent magnet he used two stationary coils wound on rubber spools. Then he adopted a coil of exceedingly fine wire for his moving element, eliminated the frame to avoid eddy currents, and reduced the turns to the lowest possible number. By fixing the pivot pins to the coil itself and swinging them in jewel bearings, he produced an element which would operate on currents so small that self-inductance was nearly, though not quite, wiped out. Finally, he added series resistance by means of a stationary coil wound noninductively in order to reduce self-inductance. With this combination, his first a-c voltmeter gave extremely promising results.

This was simply one more triumph for Weston's genius for high-precision work at a time when clumsiness and crudity were the order of the day. It was a vast surprise to his assistants when the a-c voltmeter proved a success; they had been telling him that this time he was bound to fail. His only answer was that there must be a way and that he would find it. Though they hardly believed this, they faithfully followed his directions and turned out the designs and the parts which did the job.

All that remained was to produce a commercial model, and this Weston did by reexamining every part of the instrument and refining it to the utmost for weight and balance.

The new meters were perfected and ready for production in 1891, accurate at all scale readings to ⅕ of 1 per cent. They were accepted as readily as the direct-current variety had been.

The first Weston a-c voltmeter was shipped to the Edison General Electric Lamp Works at Harrison, N. J. Very shortly it was adopted as the official standard by the Association of Edison Illuminating Companies in their Lamp Testing Bureau. If any one thing had been needed to give the instrument the country's stamp of approval, this was it. Within a very short time the Weston factory had fallen so far behind on orders for a-c instruments that customers had to wait ten months for them. Among such cheerful waiters was the Edison Company of Brooklyn. If Weston had allowed himself time for gloating over his rivals' defeats, this would have been a banner opportunity to do it.

In the tangled skein of electrical invention it is rarely possible to trace back the threads to any one man; usually a modern device is the result of vast joint effort by many minds working for many years. The portable ammeter and voltmeter of today, however, trace straight back to the laboratory on High Street in Newark, and to Edward Weston's genius for devising delicate mechanisms that worked.

In 1902, in the patent litigation which Weston brought against an imitator, the judge's opinion included this:

Few patents that come before the courts are entitled to more liberal treatment. This is a case where, upon the undisputed testimony the inventor has accomplished something which has been of unquestioned benefit to the electrical world. In an art crowded with indefatigable and brilliant enthusiasts he has made the only successful alternating-current voltmeter in use at the present day. He alone has succeeded, even against the ablest competitors which England, France and Germany could produce.

14

We now come to Weston's next important invention—the standard cell. This obscure little device, completely unknown outside the technical field, has become comparable to the standard meter bar in the vaults in Paris. It is, in fact, the gold standard of electrical measurement.

From the very beginning of his work with electricity, Weston had insisted on accuracy and excellence of workmanship. When almost every other inventor was rushing into the market with hastily rigged machines which worked poorly if they worked at all, Weston remained aloof; he was willing to charge double what his competitors did, if that was necessary to insure reliable performance. He was richly rewarded for this high purpose and, as we have seen, became the world's leading electrical instrument maker as a result.

The prime factor in this practical idealism, in which Weston set the pace for the entire scientific world, was that he was never satisfied that he had done well enough. He was forever trying to improve; while others were content to increase production and reap quick profits, he increased *values*. It was an exhausting method to pursue, for successful work was only work begun—an invitation to continue and to solve every problem again and again, always better.

From the beginning of his interest in measuring instruments, Weston had been plagued by the difficulty of obtaining a basic standard of departure. One could not build a voltmeter and calibrate it without a fundamental working definition of the volt. Long since, of course, an international agreement had been reached as to the value of the "legal" volt, ampere, and ohm. The ampere had been chosen the controlling unit and was defined as that value of current which would deposit a given fraction of a gram of silver from a plating solution in one second of time. The volt and ohm followed, by the application of Ohm's law. But for practical measurement, even in standardizing laboratories, a direct criterion had been necessary, and this had been fixed upon by the use of a "standard" electrolytic cell, or primary battery, called the Clark cell, invented about 1878. In this country, Professor H. S. Carhart of the University of Michigan had studied the means of producing the standard volt for years, and the unit was known here as the Carhart-Clark cell. It consisted simply of a glass container using electrodes of zinc and platinum immersed in the sulphates of zinc and mercury. But it had three serious shortcomings. Its voltage changed considerably with temperature, its error was uncertain because of an unknown amount of lag between voltage and temperature change, and it was highly sensitive to impurities in the zinc electrode. However, a useful cell had been developed in spite of these variables, and laboratories everywhere had adopted it as the best that could be had.

Weston first felt the annoyance of the temperature limitation when he was developing his early voltmeters in the High Street laboratory. In May, 1890, he invented and applied for a patent on an improved voltage standard which consisted of a circular glass vessel with seven small Clark cells fixed in it and held securely by a hard rubber cover. The cells were in their turn sealed into metal cans. One cell of the group was provided with a thermometer. The usual platinum and zinc electrodes were used, the electrolyte being a paste of mercurous sulphate and zinc sulphate.

The specification stated that the entire battery connected in series would produce ten legal volts at 67½ degrees Fahrenheit, or each alone would give 1.433 volts at this temperature. Weston proposed to hold the temperature constant at this value by circulating water in the outer vessel. The invention did not find wide acceptance, because of its cumbersome size and the need of a water connection at controlled temperature. But it called attention to the bothersome variation inherent in the Clark cell. Weston, the chemist, therefore got to work on a search for a better chemical composition for the cell.

Six years before, in 1884, he had made an early attempt to improve Clark's arrangement, by designing a similar cell which used an unsaturated rather than a saturated electrolyte. His reasoning was that the degree of saturation would vary with changes in temperature and so tend to hold the voltage of the cell constant. Results had been unsatisfactory, although the principle seemed to him sound.

Now, in 1893, he had time to concentrate again upon the invention of a voltage standard that was truly independent of temperature. The final result, covered by a basic patent issued in April of that year, was the Weston standard cell, now accepted throughout the world. The secret lay in the substitution of cadmium for the zinc electrode and cadmium sulphate for the corresponding zinc salt of the Clark cell. While there was still a slight temperature variation, it was twenty times smaller than with Clark's. The patent covered both saturated and unsaturated types.

A further advantage of the cadmium cell was its characteristic potential of 1.0183 volts, so close to unity that it was much easier to use in calibration work than the Clark 1.433-volt cell. Weston found that he could reproduce the same voltage in any number of identical cadmium cells within 1/100th of 1 per cent.

The new cadmium cell was first mentioned at the Chicago Exposition of 1893, where much work was done by a committee to standardize electrical units. Shortly after this the International Electrochemical Commission was formed, and serious studies of both zinc and cadmium cells were begun in laboratories here and abroad.

The Weston cell was not immediately adopted as a criterion. In fact, as studies progressed, a great deal of criticism arose. It was said to be more troublesome to construct than the Clark cell, and to suffer more voltage reduction with age. But as test data accumulated, scientific opposition diminished. The celebrated electrical measurements laboratory of the German Reichsanstalt reported in favor of the cadmium cell. Professor Carhart, who from the first had supported Weston, published a series of papers refuting the critics, who were mainly in England.

In the year 1903, the American Institute of Electrical Engineers appointed a committee to decide upon the merits of the two contenders. The committee, upon the urging of Carhart, and Carl Hering, finally selected Weston's saturated cadmium cell as the preferred standard, and petitioned Congress to make it the legal standard for the country.

Two years later, the Weston cell had been so widely accepted in all countries that the International Conference on Electrical Units and Standards also recommended it. In 1911 it finally became the official standard of electromotive force for the world.

When news of this great honor reached him, Weston published a statement waiving his patent rights in the cell, thus permitting anyone to manufacture it who was capable of doing so.

# PART FIVE

# The Man Behind the Mask

I

We have seen the highlights of Edward Weston's professional career and have briefly examined his most important inventions. But we have not seen much of the man himself, except as a silhouette behind the screen of steadily brightening electrical progress. This short biography would not be complete without an attempt, at least, to record his personality and to sketch in his human side. This is not easy, for Weston was, to all intents, a two-dimensional man, both of them lying within the plane of technology. As a human being in contact with the everyday world of emotions and pleasures, he was woefully negative—not because he never played or laughed or indulged in social intercourse, but because, when he did these things, he insisted on *engineering* them with as much vehemence as though they were design problems in electricity.

The fact is that Weston never did and never could relax mentally. His preoccupation with whatever he happened to be doing was vast and devastating. He never "took it easy" for one moment—at least, not until he was an old man—nor was anyone around him allowed to do so. His drive to accomplishment was grim and sometimes brutal; he was a man who never took a rest.

Thomas Edison has been celebrated the world over for his habit of working around the clock, snatching a nap now and then on a laboratory bench. That was not as unique in those days as the Edison myth would have us believe. In fact, Edward Weston did exactly the same thing in about the same way. It was not at all uncommon for him to remain at the instrument plant for a week at a time, when some problem refused to yield sooner. Then Mrs. Weston would be forced to bring him his meals in neatly wrapped packages, trailing young Edward along as she came. Mrs. Weston did not approve of this in the least. Not that she objected to hard work or long hours. But in all their fifty-odd years of married life she never fully understood the importance of the mechanical arts or appreciated the peculiar eagerness of an inventor's temperament. She could not see why her husband did not drop his troubles when the day was done and come home to sit, like the farmers in her native German countryside.

There was a little jealousy mixed up in her resentment of his work, and she can hardly be blamed for it. Very early in their marriage he retired into his laboratory and was never seen again, so far as her emotional needs were concerned. He was driven by the most powerful of emotions—the will to surmount obstacles and to succeed. But she had no direct part in it. There was nothing for her to do in his immensely crowded life but tend the house and bring up her children. Another type of woman would have insisted on sharing her husband's interests. Minnie Weston accepted dismissal and became, like him, a two-dimensional character, whose plane was parallel to his and so never really touched it anywhere.

On his side Edward Weston felt that his wife did not understand him. It seemed to him utterly logical that he should keep the house in a clutter of machinery and wires, and when she objected, he felt frustrated and withdrew still further into his shell. He had much natural charm, but it did not work at home. He came to believe that women were an annoyance to be avoided as much as possible. After the first flush of his romance back in the seventies he turned his back on them for the rest of his life.

There it was—the tragedy of two people who might have helped each other enormously if only they had understood each other better. It was indeed a lack of understanding, for beneath it lay a solid bedrock of loyalty that was never disturbed. Though they went grimly ahead, conceding not an inch to each other, fundamentally they believed in one another; either one would have defended the other to the limit if need had arisen. It was unfortunate that such a need did not arise. It might have pulled them together.

How definitely it was a lack of understanding is shown by Minnie Weston's parsimonious attitude toward money, and her husband's great annoyance with her for it. She was forever nagging him to cut down expenses, to save for a rainy day. He detested the mention of financial failure, because he had far more wealth than he knew what to do with, and he knew that he could always make more money if he wanted it. With no time to spend his earnings on himself, and no wifely extravagances to pay for, his fortune piled up. It got so that he did not bother to collect the damages which his many successful lawsuits poured in his lap.

2

Weston's relationship with his subordinates and employees was rather better. At the plant he was surrounded with keen and eager minds like his own. And here everybody loved him and showed their affection with quick attention and real solicitude. On his staff were a number of mathematicians, engineers, chemists, as well as many gifted artisans. They respected his every word. It was traditional in the factory that whenever the short, chunky figure of Mr. Weston, with its quick, snappy walk, hove in sight the working people turned and smiled, hoping that he would stop and talk to them and perhaps give them a hand with their job. He was always neatly dressed but without show, and the lowliest apprentice felt comfortable in his presence. It was his habit to walk through the manufacturing departments every day, stand at the shoulder of some man or girl, then gently take the work out of their hands and do it himself for a bit. Not so much in the spirit of demonstration, was this little act, as to corroborate and to give them the feeling that The Boss approved of them.

Weston was especially interested in young men, and went out of his way to help them. This tendency was accentuated by the fact that he did not get on well with his eldest son, Walter. The difficulty was a temperamental one, for Walter had inherited some of his father's own stubbornness. He had also received very hard training, being put to work too young and made to carry responsibility beyond his age. The young man was a hard worker and spent his youth in the plant, year after year, with little or no vacation. He suffered, too, from his father's terrific ambition for him, for Weston continually criticized him for failing to reach the heights he had set for him.

Walter loved and respected his father but gradually developed a defensive shield to protect himself from the ever-present criticism. This made him stubborn and morose, and eventually closed the door to an understanding between them forever.

Weston never realized what he had done to Walter. But to compensate himself for the loss, he treated many a youthful apprentice as if he were of his own blood. He even tried to help his brother-in-law, Ernest, and gave him a job making electric lamps. But he soon got into a row with him; presently he fired him. They never saw each other again.

Many were the beginners whom Weston discovered in his plant and took great pains to inspire and help. He did not believe in paying high wages and so never offered them a raise. But he did believe in higher education, and saw to it that these young men had the money and the time necessary to go to night school, buy books, and make important scientific contacts. One of his pet projects was the founding, with other prominent men of the city, of the Newark Technical School, which he financed and watched over all his life. Eventually it became the well-known Newark College of Engineering.

A special favorite of the great man during his first years as an instrument manufacturer was young Fred Runyon, son of a onetime city auditor and close friend. Fred came to work at the Williams Street meter plant in 1890, when only fifteen, starting out as a sweeper. Within two weeks he had graduated to a real job in the toolroom. But the smell of machine oil nauseated him and he got himself transferred to an assembly section, where he soon developed a method that greatly speeded up the work—for which he got himself roundly disliked by his associates, in the approved manner of today.

One day Weston sent for Fred. "Why didn't I know you were here?" he demanded. "You shouldn't be wasting your time in the assembly department. What you need is more education." Immediately he arranged for the boy to go to night school, bought him books and drafting instruments, and moved him to his own laboratory. Runyon thrived, and by 1893, when only eighteen, was put in charge of the Weston booth at the Chicago Exposition. They became almost like father and son.

Gradually Weston imbued the boy with his own philosophy of hard work, to be applied even during hours of so-called recreation. One night the protégé came to the house on what amounted to an order to play billiards. During the game he excused himself to go to the bathroom, where he found a huge dictionary conveniently placed. When he returned he remarked that it was a funny place for so important a book. "Not at all," Weston retorted solemnly. "I keep it there on purpose. It's a waste of time just sitting." At times he could be as good a "kidder" as anyone.

Waste was anathema to the inventor. He used to come and stand over Fred at his work, laying his big black cigar on the window sill and invariably forgetting it. Next day he would be back, scolding him for throwing the butt away. "An old cigar tastes just as good as a fresh one," he would say, "and it is weak-minded to waste it."

Fred Runyon left him after a few years because he needed a better salary and could easily get it elsewhere. But he never ceased to sing Weston's praises. As head of a well-known engineering firm he looked back on his severe boot training as the best possible start he could have had.

The Weston factory was probably no more noted for low wages than any other plant of that era. The spirit of the times required long, hard hours and real devotion. The enterprisers of the day knew that the young art could only survive upon a foundation of fine workmanship and deep loyalty to the cause, which is a principle that modern America may have to learn over again if it is to continue its scientific supremacy. Weston, however, believed in keeping a "happy ship" and made many provisions for recreation at noon hour and on holidays. The greatest element in this forword-looking program was a sort of interindustrial baseball league embracing many of Newark's larger plants.

Runyon himself deserves some of the credit for Weston's interest in this sensible scheme, for he induced him to furnish the uniforms and the diamond and to take a real interest in the contests himself. At one point the Sloane-Chase plant employed a toolmaker who was a marvelous pitcher and "cleaned up" on the whole league every season. Weston, as usual a perfectionist, visited a game to see why everybody was losing to this rival and immediately spotted the pitcher. After the game he broke a company rule by offering the man five dollars a week more than he was receiving—and got him. After that the Instrument Company topped the league.

In all this Weston did not forget his younger son, whom he had so proudly piloted across Brooklyn Bridge to see the new arc-light installations. Edward, only ten when the instrument factory was opened, gave every sign of following in his father's footsteps, and received all the attention that Weston saved for young men he sponsored. Edward was always tagging after his mother to the plant, often staying the day out, to return home with his father at night. He was fascinated by the delicate manufacturing operations; more especially he was delighted with the smooth organization which sent the products out to a sure and growing market.

Edward remembers back to a day when he was no more than five, when his mother took him along on a trip to the old Plane Street lamp plant. Here he was immediately entranced with the glass-blowing operation; before long he was a regular visitor in that department and had many friends among the Bohemian experts who sat all day long at their benches and twisted glowing glass tubes in the Bunsen flames. One of them taught Edward a neat trick brought over from the old country—a glass swan quickly blown out of a small piece of tubing, with the end of the pipe sticking out for a tail. Just behind the proudly arched head, the glass blower would puncture a little hole and the job was finished. You filled the swan with water, then gave it to a crony with instructions to blow very hard and produce a lovely whistle. A good puff would send a quick spurt of water out of the little hole into the surprised whistler's eye. A delightful trick it was, and a sure way to earn the admiration of one's school companions, for whom Edward was glad to have a great many glass swans made.

Every art has its peculiar trade-mark, bound up in the human foibles of the men who pursue it. Electric lamp bulbs in those days displayed small brown bubbles, cast securely in the glass and quite ineradicable. These were called "beer spots," and had to be tolerated as long as the Bohemian artisans controlled the trade. The spots were accurately named; the glassblowers spent their lunch hours drinking beer and when they returned to work would joyfully belch carbon dioxide and beer into their blowpipes as they worked the hot glass. Weston tried to train girls to the blowing, but they made a mess of it till metal molds were invented to control the shape of the bulbs. After that beer spots became a museum curiosity avidly sought by historians of the early electric days.

Edward grew up and into the Weston business as naturally as the beer spots themselves, and when his father retired in 1924, became its president and, later, chairman of the board.

3

Though Weston never went in for politics in his adopted city, he was extremely public-spirited whenever a technical advance was in prospect for Newark. More than once his scientific knowledge and his expertness in court brought great advantage to the town. He was one of the principal organizers, stockholders, and officers in the Newark District Telegraph Company, started by Fred Runyon's uncle, Frederick T. Fearey. Like many other similar systems, this one had circuits to all parts of town and sold messenger and burglar-alarm service to banks and stores.

Fearey was the moving spirit in many important business ventures in Newark, among them the local telegraph office. One of his most fruitful projects in the expansion of the city was a cigar store, which he had opened in the center of town for the benefit of his war-crippled brother. The store was the favorite gathering place for reporters, editors, and financiers during the downtown lunch hour. Here, under the Feareys' guidance, many an important civic project was born.

It was in Fearey's cigar store that the plans were hatched in the eighties for a local telephone company, operating under a franchise from the Bell interests. The Newark Domestic Telephone and Telegraph Company was duly organized, with Fearey and Weston among its promoters, and most of the leading citizens as investors. The venture was very successful and highly profitable; at one time it had more crossarms on its poles [and hence more circuits and subscribers] than any other telephone system in America, except the New York Telephone Company itself.

The Bell interests, at this time, were sending missionaries all over the country, persuading local businessmen to organize their own companies under a ten-year franchise, using Bell patents and equipment. Then, when the companies were on their feet and showing a good profit, the New York people would buy them up and operate them at a better profit still. When Newark's franchise ran out, Weston and his friends, being fully aware of what they had, demanded a renewal, as provided for in the original papers. Bell refused, and the Newark Company, probably at Weston's urging, sued them. The inventor performed as the star witness with such telling effect that the company won. Then the Newark people sold out to Bell for three dollars on the dollar. The parent company was perfectly aware that even at this extraordinary markup they were making a profitable deal. Newark Tel. and Tel. was one of the best-run engineering properties in the United States.

If Weston had needed any further recommendation in the eyes of his townsmen, he had it now. They were very grateful to him indeed. The certainty that he knew what he was about earned him a host of friends and made him the most celebrated and respected scientist in a city which had contributed more useful inventions than any other town in America.

## 4

But even a man as absorbed in his work as Edward Weston could not work all the time. Occasionally he had to play in spite of himself. He did not take to it easily, and would never have done it at all if his health had not broken down periodically and thrown him into the hands of a doctor who straightway ordered him on a vacation. The old trouble with his eyes kept cropping up, and after the fracas with the United States Lighting people in 1886, nervous breakdowns plagued him continually.

Weston regarded vacations with horror and disdain; he "solved" them with the same grim determination to succeed that he used in his laboratory. Consequently he did not enjoy them, and succeeded only in making himself and whomever he chose to take along with him, miserable. He never took a vacation except by doctor's prescription.

During his active years the only "vacation" he could tolerate was to go fishing, and this he did with an energy and expertness born of desperation. Weston could never permit himself to be a duffer at anything; he was no novice at fishing, after the first experience.

Once when he was ordered off for a month's rest, he chose the Rangeley Lakes, taking Walter with him. His fishing kit included everything from a 2⅞-ounce fly-rod [the lightest ever made] to a harpoon. Not being sure of the variety of fish in the Maine lakes, he wished to be fully prepared. When he got there he hired a guide, though the Rangeleys, even in that day, were rather thickly surrounded by summer people, villages, and stores. He did not make a record catch on the expedition, and never went to Maine again.

Gradually Weston got to *like* fishing and counted himself an expert at fly casting, which he came as near enjoying as he did anything outside his work. He tried nearly every well-known body of water in the East, dropping each one instantly if it did not give him immediate results. Seabright, N. J., was one of his haunts; so was Atlantic City. Neither satisfied him. Finally, he settled upon Greenwood Lake, an isolated little place some forty miles north of Newark. There was an old guide there who "knew every fish by name," and whom Weston hired, rowboat, biceps, and all. While the old native rowed steadily around the lake, he would cast doggedly for hours till he had caught or repulsed every hungry fish in the pond. It was an exhausting experience; the guide took it calmly only because he was a wilderness philosopher.

One way or another Weston exposed himself to practically every form of gentleman's sport, from owning and riding a horse through Newark traffic to parading down Fifth Avenue in a top hat and full beard, swinging a tight-furled umbrella. This latter had been his earliest form of recreation and was soon abandoned. But it left him with a feeling that he should occasionally exhibit himself in public for the benefit of his own morale and the neighbors' edification. The horse expanded into an elegant rig, both carryall and sleigh, with the inventor silently managing the reins as he drove his equally silent family out on a fine Sunday.

Later, driving struck him as too costly for the small good he got out of it, so he took to a bicycle, experimenting with every American make and finally sending abroad for both Humber and Swift makes. He was one of the first to "risk his life" on a "safety"—the earliest form of bicycle with two wheels the same size. With this and numerous later models he rode determinedly all over northern

New Jersey, spending whole weekends at it sometimes. Not satisfied with that, he joined a bike club and submitted to the grueling "runs" that were popular before the motorcycle infested the planet. Edward Weston was an extremist when it came to sport, working it to death until he had got everything possible out of it, then dropping it overnight for something else that was new.

Bicycling was followed in due course by automobiling. Weston was never one to wait until an invention had turned commonplace; he was always up in front, trying out the early, scatterbrained models. So it was with the horseless buggy. His first venture in automobiling was taken about 1901, and the car a Columbia, Mark 8. As in everything else, he had combed the market for what he thought the soundest engineering job and had chosen this contraption because it advertised itself as combining the best features of the European makes.

The Columbia was the first car to get the engine out from under the seat and put it in front. This power plant was mounted on springs to prevent its vibrations from shaking the passengers to pieces; the resilience would often bring on a rhythmic convulsion so violent that the gasoline was jounced clear out of the carburetor. Then the car would hesitate while gasoline fumes collected in the muffler. A deafening explosion rearward would then signal its return to life, and the Columbia would lurch forward through Newark, Weston like a cast-iron figure gripping the wheel, and horses up and down the street rearing and neighing and dragging carriage wheels over curbs. It was a lurid but brief episode in the inventor's life. Like everything else, he gave it up as soon as he felt he had mastered it, and later joined the millions of car owners without flourish.

## 5

Edward Weston could no more take second place in the department of personal skill than he could in engineering. If he went in for a sport at all it was in the vigorous belief that he could master it completely. And so he did, in more than one instance. Trapshooting seemed to be his outstanding road to local fame. Once it had been brought to his attention, he immediately bought all sorts of shotguns and joined the South Side Gun Club, which had a hut on the Jersey meadows. For a long time he went there religiously every Saturday and Sunday, banging away at the clay pigeons with such rapidly improving aim that he got to be top man in the club and wore a gold pigeon with a paper tail in his buttonhole.

There wasn't a shotgun made that Weston had not examined; he owned an arsenal of them. In those days sportsmen made their own shells, loading them with powder and shot according to personal formula. Weston got to puzzling over the matter, decided to be scientific about it, and began an elaborate piece of research into the effect of varying the ingredients. He was working for the United States Company at the time; in the cellar of the plant was a little flat car that ran on narrow-gauge track to handle freight. Weston took this over, mounted several shotguns on it and then banged away at paper targets on the wall, studying the shot patterns that resulted from his experimental shell loadings fired from different ranges. Sometimes when the Chief Electrician's advice or instructions were needed and he couldn't be found, and everyone was running up and downstairs looking for him, there would come a mighty roar from the cellar. Then Young or Stevens or some other loyal assistant would say, "There's your man, down in the Ordnance Department. But you'll get your head blown off if you go down after him."

It was this painstaking if noisy research which won Weston the shooting prize on the Meadows. Once the honor was his, he lost interest and quit cold.

Billiards and golf he took in the same spirit. To become expert with the cue he joined the Chatelet Club and spent night after night, practicing interminably till he was the best shot in the place. Progress toward this end being too slow to suit him, he purchased a billiard table of his own, set it up in his High Street home, and played constantly, getting some young fellow like Fred Runyon to act as an opponent just to keep the game alive.

Weston's endurance during his expert rages was phenomenal; even the young men he befriended could not keep up. During the billiard period the impish side of his character was in full flood. Having worked intensely for a week on some invention, he would suddenly knock off late in the afternoon, gather up his laboratory assistants, then hustle them to a downtown restaurant and stuff them with a magnificent dinner, fully garnished with beer or wine. Hardly able to stand up under this cargo, the young men would be dragged to a pool hall and made to play literally till they dropped. Next morning, while they were so groggy they could hardly go to work, Weston would gallop into the plant as if nothing out of the ordinary had happened at all.

With golf it was the same, though the machinery of the game was rather more cumbersome. He joined a country club, of course. There he found that what seemed easy—driving the ball in the desired direction and to the right distance—was indeed impossible for him. This made him furious; he decided that the clubs were badly designed. Calling in his chief engineer, Goodwin—this was now about 1906 and the instrument company was well seasoned and profitable —he outlined an elaborate series of studies on the center of inertia and percussion effect in golf clubs. Goodwin dutifully sidetracked his meter work in order to make the research, eventually came out with new designs. When the clubs were made, Weston got even worse scores with them than he had with the commercial variety. His answer was to set himself a terrific schedule of practice, which included dragging his caddy, Bud, to the links at five in the morning all one summer and shooting as many as two hundred balls, one after the other, before breakfast. Weston's health was so poor at this time that he could not stoop to tee up his own shots. Finally he moved to the club and lived there, practicing golf exclusively.

Results still proving unsatisfactory, he moved back home and began practicing stance on a canvas ground cloth specially made for him till he had worked out what he thought was the most scientific position. When the club pro disagreed with him about it, he collected all the pros from the surrounding clubs and brought them to his house for a conference. The meeting was a dud, for the pros did not believe that stance was the secret of good golf at all. Then Weston sent a man to Scotland to buy up the finest old clubs to be had in the land of the game's origin. When these did not improve his game he quit, reluctantly admitting that he had exploited his potential skill to its utmost.

Golf was the one game that competed with Edward Weston and came out ahead. He never forgave it for this ungallant act.

But he restored his confidence by becoming an unquestioned expert at photography. Ever since his early days in New York he had understood the chemistry of picture taking, and the delight in snapping a camera shutter never left him. It was the only hobby that followed him loyally all through life.

Weston owned every conceivable camera, plate, film, and chemical, and shelf upon shelf of lenses, foreign and domestic. He took hundreds of pictures of the same object—nothing more interesting, usually, than a tree in the back yard, striving continually for photographic excellence, and utterly indifferent to any pleasure which the pictures might give later on. He was not interested in records of events or in the pictorial value of a scene, but only in the technical perfection of the result. Not a single picture survives that is worth more than a cursory glance.

Thus was this strange genius driven by his demanding nature to seek improvement in every skill and process he touched, ignoring the relaxation of a hobby in the furious pursuit of expertness. It was tragic for him that he could not simply have fun. All living was work to him, all the world an engineering graph on which he was impelled to draw only ascending curves of achievement. The one partial exception to this was yachting. He did enjoy that for its own sake, and followed the sport keenly for more than forty years.

## 6

There was only one thing that Edward Weston really loved and enjoyed, and that was a fight. The struggle to master a hobby was too weak to suit him; the solution to his scientific problems too easy or too readily delegated to others. What he craved was personal struggle; like a wrestler who will not step onto the mat till he is confronted with an opponent of equal weight and skill, he wanted something that would use every ounce of his ability, enclose him in a hammer lock that could be broken only by utter victory or complete defeat.

That is why Weston perpetually involved himself in patent suits. Here at last he found the opportunity to use his utmost strength.

He would go into court over a shoe button or the fundamentals of electric power with equal zest and at the drop of a hat, then omit to collect when the case was won. If he had no battles of his own he would take on somebody else's just as eagerly. It was the fight itself which gave him his sense of completeness and power.

Weston wasn't a very good churchman. Unlike Michael Faraday, whom he worshiped, he found religious formality at odds with science and chose the latter throughout. Though he often dragged his whole family to church, it was only a stiff formality that impelled him. He chose the Universalist faith, which seemed to him the most liberal. But he had several minister friends, and one of these was the Reverend Hannibal Goodwin of the Newark House of Prayer. Weston was not impressed by his spiritual views but liked him because he had invented the celluloid photographic film and was in a fight with George Eastman over the patents to it. Goodwin had offered to sell out to Eastman and had been turned down. The good minister would come to Weston's laboratory and walk the floor, inveighing against the Kodak magnate in most unclerical language and begging Weston to tell him what to do. The inventor's answer was simply: "Fight 'em!"

So Goodwin fought them, through the Ansco Company, to whom he had meanwhile sold his patents. The suit is said to have lasted for twenty years and to have ended in a multimillion dollar settlement—on paper. But by that time Goodwin was dead.

Edward Weston was glad to lend fuel to other people's fires but really preferred to start a legal conflagration of his own. Once he got into a litigation over a fishing rod and won. It was a Gilbert and Sullivan affair which started abruptly one day as he was setting off on a fishing "vacation" with his son Edward. Among the welter of tackle and gear that accompanied them to the railroad station was a special fishing rod in a leather case with a padlock. Though they were only going to Lake Hopatcong, the station agent refused to check the rod on Weston's ticket, saying that it was freight, not baggage, and must go by express. Weston went livid with rage; train after train went off without the vacationists while the argument over the rod grew hot. Finally, he left it behind and boarded a train. But he endured the trip only for the sake of getting back and going into court against the railroad for failure to live up to the printed contract on its tickets. The suit dragged on for months, with everybody in the plant testifying, including small Edward. It was a jury case and the jury finally found for Weston. The judge awarded him six cents and costs. But he had won and had had immense satisfaction doing it.

Not only the railroads but every other business firm came to know Weston as a bad man to cross in an argument. He was too apt to take offense over a small injustice and to cost them thousands in court. Needless to say, Weston ignored the six cents. He was just as apt to ignore favorable judgments of thousands of dollars. The fight was what he wanted.

Legal warfare was not only a fine technical exercise for him; it was his one opportunity to exert his personality to the full upon the personalities of others. Once he met a man in court who had worked for him and had absconded with an invention and made a success of it in a rival concern. "Hello, Mr. Weston," said the offender, offering his hand. The inventor gave him one sharp look and put both hands in his pockets. "I only shake hands with people I respect," he growled.

No inventor of that day who had made his mark failed to come to blows with the great Thomas Edison. Weston began early with this fight and continued it till the onrush of electrical engineering had left them both far behind. He did not regard it as a struggle between Edison's patents and his own, but as a personal feud. To him Edison was no scientist but a promoter who "grabbed everything that was not nailed down." He hated him so bitterly that when he was named a recipient of the Edison medal by the American Institute of Electrical Engineers, he refused it.

Edison was rather amused at all this. A mutual friend called on him one day and mentioned a recent stricture that Weston had made against him. "I guess his liver must be out," he remarked.

"Shucks!" laughed Edison, "his liver is always out. It's been out for twenty years."

A good deal of the litigation, of course, was necessary to defend the commercial position of the contending parties. During the early 1900's the Instrument Company actually had sixty-four suits in court at the same time. Its whole future hung in the balance, for every competitor had appropriated the Weston instrument in detail, from the ageing of the magnets to the Manganin shunt. Although the company's finances were sound and its sales strong, it could not muster the money to fight General Electric and Westinghouse. Weston smartly compromised by starting separate suits against his weaker opponents first, picking them off one by one and gradually establishing a body of evidence by which to confound the big fellows later on. His judgment was sound; in every case, by intense application and the devotion of all his time and strength, he won. Finally he stood on top, having beaten small fry and giants alike, and making the Weston Electrical Instrument Company the unassailable leader in its field.

It was not till Westinghouse and General Electric were forced to pay royalties on the manufacture of instruments that the Weston Company attained the leading position in the industry, which it has held ever since. That victory would never have been secured if Edward Weston himself had not fought on, year after year, oblivious of the cost, oblivious of everything but to win.

## 7

If it had not been for Edward Weston's pugnacious drive to down every opponent in court, his fortunes would undoubtedly have failed. But he won everywhere because a legal fight was one thing he refused to delegate. He took on every suit personally, fought them with a furious energy which involved everyone near him and cost his subordinates many a sleepless night. As his inventive career closed, his legal one blossomed. He became a professional fighter; if a battle was not handy at the moment, he would make one. The start of the famous Jewell shunt case, which set the whole instrument litigation in motion in 1899, was a brazen punch on the nose administered by Weston upon Jewell to furnish an incident upon which to begin a war. He was looking far ahead and his strategy was masterly from the start.

In his testimony in this suit he said:

My application for a patent [on a voltmeter] was filed with the express intention of bringing about an interference between Mr. Jewell and myself, and the drawings shown in Jewell's patent were taken and embodied almost exactly in my application for the purpose of insuring an interference. I had no desire to obtain a patent embodying the features of the several issues here in dispute and so stated this to Mr. Kintner [his lawyer]. For I had to take this opportunity while the proofs were still in existence and the witnesses were available, to establish priority of invention of all the several devices embodied. . . . I deemed this necessary in view of the menace to our business arising from Jewell's patent.

This statement, made for the benefit of the patent examiners, did not secure Weston a new patent—which he did not want—but brought out invaluable testimony in his behalf, which he immediately set out to use in court.

The elaborate care which he took to prepare himself sometimes reached fantastic proportions. He always went into the background of a case with terrifying thoroughness, reading volumes and poring over articles and catalogues until he had the entire matter at his fingertips. Once a magazine published some very minor criticism of him. Minor or not, he sued them, and in the course of it made Caxton Brown, then manager of the New York office, write an entire brochure on the subject of the original slight.

He was even harder on himself in preparatory work. Using sheets of cheap yellow paper, he would write page after page of exposition and argument to familiarize himself with the points he wanted to make on the stand. A glue pot always stood open on his desk; as each sheet was filled with his energetic longhand, he would paste an empty one to the bottom of it and go on writing, pushing the finished stuff over the back of the desk. Often he reeled off twenty or thirty feet of the stuff before he was satisfied.

When the manuscript was finished, Weston would call in young Goodwin or some other official and make him listen to the whole thing. Sometimes the job would not be finished till every one had left the plant. Then Weston would roll the script up and take it home. There James, the butler, would be the victim, standing stiffly against the wall of his master's study into the small hours while the unintelligible jargon was read to him.

John Hardin, the firm's principal lawyer, eventually became worried about the immense amount of time wasted in listening to

Weston's outpourings. Hoping to put a hint in his head, he sent Weston a huge bill for extra time spent at this unprofitable task. Weston failed to take the hint. So Hardin made his next bill even worse. This time the boss sent for him. "Your rates are going up, John," he complained. "Don't forget you're a vice president of the firm."

"Doctor," pleaded Hardin, "it was the only way I could think of to teach you not to waste our time."

But the lesson was never learned. And when the shunt case was won and the company immensely strengthened thereby, nobody had an argument left.

## 8

The shunt case against the Empire Electrical Instrument Company and its officers was probably the most important litigation Weston ever entered, and in it his histrionic talents were at their best, and his preparation complete. Empire had been making shunt-type instruments, as everybody else had, on the assumption that Weston had patented something already in the public domain. At least, this was their *stated* assumption. It was established later that they were perfectly aware of the infringement, but assumed that if everybody else infringed, Weston would find the situation hopeless and give up the fight. They had seriously misjudged him; the mistake cost them their business.

Eight or ten Weston suits were brought against Empire in all, covering, one by one, the patents on electric instruments. The shunt was only one of them, but the definitive one. It was first brought in 1901, and as usual, dragged on for a number of years.

Early in the game Weston realized that he was dealing with crooks. It appeared that one of Empire's principal backers, F. A. La Roche, had approached Charles D. Cooke, a manufacturer of locomotives, and had persuaded him that he had valuable patents covering electrical instruments. On the strength of this, Cooke had organized the Empire Company and La Roche had accepted stock in it in return for the patents. Manufacturing had begun in 1899, continuing for about five years thereafter.

It was not until January, 1903, that La Roche himself had been tracked down and brought to the stand. Here he had proved to be a most plausible witness, giving glib accounts of his "invention" of shunt-type instruments as far back as 1888. These, he testified, he had installed in various power plants in Philadelphia. The judge accepted him in good faith.

In later testimony, given when the case was still in full swing in 1907, Weston related:

> On the day that Mr. La Roche first appeared on the witness stand, which, if my recollection is correct, was Friday, January 2nd, 1903, Mr. William H. Kenyon [his lawyer] called me upon the telephone from New York, and stated that Mr. La Roche had concluded his direct testimony in that case, and the following morning—Saturday, January 3rd—I read the testimony, and from that time on I took up the subject of this shunt case and spent almost the whole of nine months of my time in prosecuting and directing the investigation to elicit the truth of the allegations made by La Roche . . . and in assisting and preparing the matter for the cross-examination of La Roche. Almost all of the cross-questions submitted to La Roche were drawn by me while living at the Waldorf.

Weston had moved into New York to the old Waldorf on 34th Street, in order to give his whole time to the affair.

In those nine months La Roche was sick a great deal and at crucial moments could not appear on the stand for cross-examination. Weston, suspicious of this, had him followed by detectives and discovered that when the man was supposed to be ill in bed he was actually drinking in bars or going to the theater.

Although he was virtually certain that he could win the case, Weston, with characteristic thoroughness, set himself grimly to track down every shred of evidence. Here was a perfect case of patent piracy, offering a clear opportunity to show up the sharp practices so prevalent in the young electrical industry. He was willing to devote all his time and any amount of money to making a thorough exposé of the whole affair.

Systematically Weston traced every one of La Roche's statements to its source, particularly his claims that he had installed instruments of his own invention in power stations. Long search was necessary, but his scouts eventually found the men who had erected and operated the plants. Every one of them denied all knowledge of La Roche instruments or that instruments of any kind had been used. This proved that the man had been committing perjury on the stand.

Discovered, La Roche became a more willing witness, and gradually the truth came to light. But it would never have done so without Weston.

"I wrote most of the [cross-] questions during the night," he related, "frequently working all night, getting my reports from parties that were investigating the case, and framing my questions largely upon these reports. After the examination of the day, Mr. Bissing and Mr. Benneke came to my rooms and read from the testimony that had been taken. When questions were not satisfactorily replied to, I pointed out wherein I thought we needed further information. From many of the answers during that day I framed the questions that night, and from further reports received, added new ones on these subjects. My only chance for sleep was, most of the time, in the daytime, and not very much at that, because I had to have my rough manuscript put into typewritten form and had to look over that before it was turned over to counsel and my technical assistant, Mr. Benneke, for the next day's work. When the examination was not going on, I made it my special purpose to make visits wherever I could glean information at first hand, myself. I visited the various establishments, or buildings, where La Roche had been located, measured the dimensions of the buildings, determined what portions had been occupied by other businesses, and what portions had been available for occupation by the business he had alleged he had carried on. Where changes had been made in the buildings, I ascertained those facts and the nature of the changes, and found the parties who had made them. In this way I checked the accuracy or inaccuracy of any statement he had made in regard to machinery allegedly used by him in any one of the places in the production of any part or all of the alleged anticipating devices. I had carefully analyzed the exhibits put in the case as alleged prior anticipations of the devices, and each part thereof, and knew precisely what operations and what tools were required to do the work on each part, and whether it was possible, therefore, for him to have had those tools in those places. I had made investigations as to the nature of the sources of electric current he had alleged to have used, such as dynamos and batteries, and of the power required to run the dynamos, and the power of the engine he would have needed to run them to produce the results that he asserted he had got from them. I had computed the heating effect of the currents that he said he had used on certain of the alleged anticipating shunts, and I had determined it experimentally on exact duplicates of those shunts. I had made duplicates of the shunts and put these in the hands of competent searchers to take around to be shown the people who had used plants erected by La Roche and I had photographs in the hands of these searchers of the instruments with which the shunts were alleged to be used, and those were carried around in precisely the same way, and for the same purpose, namely, to elicit the exact truth. In this way, I tackled every branch of the case, personally directed it and largely conducted it. The labor was enormous. No fact, I think, would be likely to escape my attention or my memory in regard to it, especially where I have an opportunity to refer to the original documents before me."

In June, 1904, an interlocutory decree was handed down, enjoining the Empire and La Roche companies from further infringement of the shunt invention and appointing Samuel N. Hitchcock as Special Master to review all the evidence and set the damages. Hitchcock held hearings for two more years, during which time La Roche died. His report to the court corroborated all previous findings and established the guilt of the Empire and La Roche companies.

This meant the ruin of both. Their businesses were disbanded and their tools and plants sold.

But Weston was still not satisfied, because he had not yet succeeded in bringing punishment upon any individual. He now went after Cooke personally, successfully petitioning the court to reopen the hearings before the Special Master for the purpose of involving Cooke himself.

Way back in 1901 Cooke had gathered together as many as possible of the instrument companies Weston was suing, hoping to pool their resources in one grand fight for existence. Weston had absolutely refused to deal with them collectively, knowing full well that to divide was to conquer. Cooke had then offered to sell him the Empire company outright. This had infuriated Weston all the more; it was tantamount to buying his own inventions from the thief who stole them.

But at this time he had not suspected Cooke himself. "I believed him to be an honorable man, and that he had been misled. . . ."

Cooke had come to Weston's Newark office to plead in person. Weston would not hear of a sale, but devoted several hours to acquainting him with La Roche's duplicity. "I told him that I thought it was about time that he looked into the case himself."

Cooke had left, apparently determined to do so. There was an interval of *four years* now; in March, 1907, the case was reopened for the last time. For the next twelve months Weston worked harder than ever to amass evidence; he dug up the entire testimony again, went over it, filled in the weak spots, directed his attorneys in every move, practically wrote every question for them, as he had done before.

The final result was the triumph he had spent seven years to achieve. The Master found that "Cooke was not only one of the original defendants named in the bill of complaint . . . and entirely failed to exercise reasonable diligence to ascertain the actual facts and see justice done, but that he thereafter continued to advance money in support of the defense of the suit.

"There would be a failure of justice if the plaintiff, who has seen its patents boldly appropriated for a number of years, should be denied relief against an individual through whose pernicious activity it has been made to suffer the consequent loss. I find therefore, that judgment should be entered against the defendant, Cooke. . . ."

It was upon this finding that Weston was able to base the entire structure of his battle against the host of infringers of his instrument business. There is no doubt that his dogged fight to make the case complete and all-inclusive was a major factor in cleaning up the mess into which patent litigation had fallen in the formative years of the electrical art.

9

It would be inaccurate to call Edward Weston a lonely or even a solitary man. His life, as we have shown, was crammed with activity and with continual striving for success and the winning of it. He knew thousands of people, among them the most prominent engineers and scientists of his day. To a man they respected him, and many loved him. But it is doubtful whether any knew him intimately or shared his personal confidence. Weston lived unto himself, like a figure being carried swiftly down a broad river in a very small boat.

He had no cronies, in the accepted sense. Colleagues, coworkers, subordinates, but no bosom friends with whom to discuss the state of the nation and of the world.

When he did come out of his workroom it was to receive an honor richly deserved and too often long overdue. Such was his election to the presidency of the American Institute of Electrical Engineers, in 1888. The Institute was founded in 1884, as one way to relieve the rapidly worsening patent situation. Responsible electricians everywhere felt that by banding together and discussing their differences they could avoid much litigation and cut down the bitternesses and misunderstandings. Weston was a charter member of the organization. Having joined as an associate, he was advanced to full membership within a few months, then placed on the first Board of Directors. For the following three years he was manager and then became President for a year, the limit of tenure specified in the by-laws. Following that, he served a year as Vice-President. He was steadily active in Institute affairs, at one time heading a committee which ejected the notorious La Roche from membership.

Weston's membership in other prominent engineering groups ran about the same as for most men of scientific prominence. They included the American Society of Mechanical Engineers, the American Electrochemical Society, American Physical Society, American Chemical Society, the Franklin Institute, and the American Association for the Advancement of Science, of which he became a fellow. He was more active in the Electrochemical Society and the Franklin Institute than in the others. Besides these, he belonged to several still more specialized organizations, such as the American Geographical

Society, the Illuminating Engineering Society, the Society for the Promotion of Engineering Education, and the National Electric Light Association. Honorary memberships were accorded to him in various other groups: the American Museum of Natural History, the Metropolitan Museum of Arts, the Inventors Guild, the Newark Board of Trade, and the Society for the Encouragement of Arts, in England. He did considerable work for the Guild on its membership committee.

He was on every list of prominent professional men, and was frequently invited to shindigs for which he had little time and less inclination, though he was always most exemplary in acknowledging the honor. Such was the elaborate "breakfast" in New York in honor of Prince Henry of Prussia, on February 26, 1902. This gala affair occupied Sherry's entire establishment and turned out a glittering roster of the city's elite. Weston broke a rigid rule and went. But he listened to the speeches with only one ear; he was absorbed in shunts and litigation, much more important to him than welcoming visiting firemen.

So devoted was Weston to his own affairs, and so little given to publicizing himself, that he was nearly unknown to the world in general. But his name was far from unknown to the scientific fraternity and especially to the men of higher education.

"It gives me very much pleasure," wrote Dean H. T. Bovey of the Faculty of Applied Science of McGill University, "to inform you that this afternoon the Corporation of McGill University decided to confer upon you the honorary Degree of Doctor of Laws, at the Convocation to be held on April 29th." This was in 1904.

Weston's reply was typical in its gratitude and humility. In part he wrote:

> I assure you that I cannot express in words to you and to the other eminent scientific men composing the Faculty of McGill University, my full appreciation of the high honor conferred upon me. Nor do I know how to appropriately and adequately thank you and the other friends who have been so kind as to remember me and my humble work in the electrical field, and to take so much interest and trouble in my behalf.

He was as delighted as any other man at being immortalized, as only a great university can do it.

Weston's affection for McGill, his first honorary alma mater, continued, and he gave much time and thought to the welfare of the University science department, even to the point of seeking an assistant from among its faculty. In April of 1907, the University suffered a disastrous fire, losing most of its buildings, including its large technical library. Weston immediately telegraphed his sympathy and offered help. When the time came to rebuild he gave a large sum of money and a complete set of standardizing instru-' ments for the new laboratory.

A degree of Doctor of Science followed, in the same year, from nearby Stevens Institute of Technology in Hoboken.

The third and most signal honor accorded Edward Weston in the academic world came to him from Princeton University in 1910, during the presidency there of Woodrow Wilson. Through the good offices of Professor Charles F. Brackett, he was named a recipient of the degree of Doctor of Science. Brackett was an old friend; on several occasions he had come to New York to appear as an expert witness in the various instrument suits. He had the highest regard for Weston's genius.

Characteristically, the inventor kept Brackett waiting for an acknowledgement.

> My tardiness in writing you [he finally replied] has not been due to want of courtesy or appreciation, but rather to the fact that I have been intensely occupied in pushing to completion a very large number of new instruments and in prosecuting a very elaborate series of new researches on resistance alloys. . . . Indeed I may truly say that I have never been so busy as I have been since last September, and my physical and mental endurance have been taxed to the utmost limit in carrying on personally and directing this work.
>
> I have found new resistance alloys much superior to anything I previously discovered . . . Manganin is a thing of the past. But so also are most of my favorite working hypotheses, things of the past.
>
> You see, at sixty, I am still in harness and I find I can endure more labor than either of my sons.

At sixty, active as ever, putting off the pleasant duty of receiving a first-rate honor in order to improve on something already the standard of the world! Weston was a true scientist.

On June 14, 1910, he received his degree at Princeton, along with two old friends and electrical pioneers—Elihu Thomson and Frank Sprague. But even at Princeton we do not find him relaxing and merely enjoying the sunlight of high praise. He spent much of his time discussing galvanometers with Professor Augustus Trowbridge of the Physics Department—a discussion which led to much later correpondence.

Not less desirable, if somewhat quieter, were the professional honors given to Weston by the technical societies. The first came to him in the Princeton year, 1910, from the Franklin Institute. This was the Elliott Cresson medal, accorded "in recognition of your brilliant and successful research in the field of electrical discovery."

"And also," said Dr. R. B. Owens, Secretary of the Institute, "in recognition of the indomitable energy you have so lavishly and so effectively expended throughout a period of nearly half a century in the advancement of the applications of electricity to fill the needs of and supply the wants of an ever-increasingly complicated and exacting civilization."

Of greater significance, perhaps, was the honor which came in 1915, at the hands of the Society of Chemical Industry, on January 22. He appreciated it all the more, since chemistry had been his first love, and since all his work had been done with the fineness of touch and appreciation of minute detail which a scientist dealing with the fundamental particles of nature could command.

The occasion was, indeed, a summing up of all his work, a kind of capstone to his career. It was the more telling because it was staged and watched over by his first friend in America—Professor Chandler of Columbia—the man who had got him his first job with Murdock in 1870.

No man was ever lionized more fully than was Weston that night, with Chandler, Leo H. Baekeland, and Carl Hering giving lengthy biographical sketches of his work, each as it appealed to him. Then Weston himself got up. If his voice ever shook, if his armor of de-

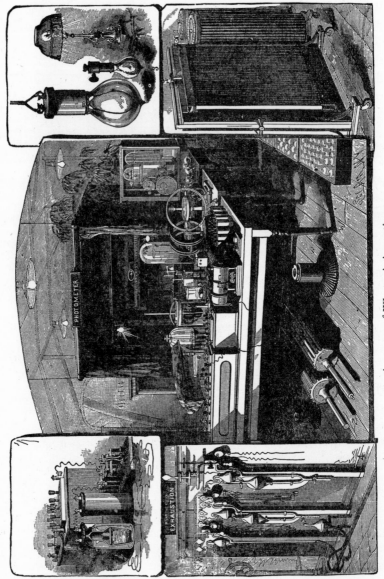

A group of Weston's inventions.

tachment and of concentration ever cracked, they did so now, as he addressed himself directly to Chandler.

"Dr. Chandler, it is nearly 45 years since I first met you. You were then Professor of Chemistry at the School of Mines in the old Columbia College Building. I was then just out of my teens and, only a short time before, I had left the land of my birth in order to escape from parental coercion intended to compel me to continue to follow a profession which I intensely disliked . . . and to carve out there, in my own way, a career in directions which I had previously diligently pursued and really loved. Tonight you have most kindly and appreciatingly referred to my career and work and you have presented me with this beautiful Perkin Medal. I thank you most sincerely for both. But I wish also to now publicly express to you my thanks and my deep sense of gratitude for the gracious manner in which you received me when, in the year 1870, I was a solitary stranger in a strange land. . . . In your long, useful and honorable professional career, I know you have frequently done for others what you then did for me, and I assure you that I have never forgotten, but always have cherished the memory of the kindness and real service you did me then."

What a situation! To be able to dramatize and round up an entire career in terms of thanks to a man who had given him a start and who had remained his friend, to watch him make good upon that start and become one of the great geniuses in an alien land already packed with them! A boy who had landed at the Battery with a family Bible and a few pounds of English money, and who now could count his fortune in the production of more than 300 patents and in comfortable wealth.

Two more important recognitions came to him during the gentle downward slope of his life. One was the highest award within the power of the Franklin Institute to give: the Franklin medal, which carried with it Honorary Membership in the Institute. The occasion, held in Philadelphia on the twenty-first of May, 1924, was unique in that Weston shared the honor with another great Englishman, Sir Ernest Rutherford, the world's leading physicist. The combination of these two was more especially fitting, since the new science of atomic physics, unfolding in laboratories the world over, could not move forward at all without the precise electrical-measurement techniques in which Weston was the pioneer and master technician.

Weston fell seriously ill a few days before the ceremony and could not be present. His old friends, Dr. Frank Sprague and Dr. Leo Baekeland, stood in his place. Sprague said: "I have gladly come here to join, insofar as lies in my power, in paying tribute to one of the greatest lights in the electrical field, a man whose name is a household word wherever accuracy of quantitative measurements is necessary, one who by his individual work has contributed more to the facility of carrying on the electrical industry than any other I know.

"He is one of a trio of famous men of foreign birth, one of whom —a great Belgian, Doctor Baekeland—is here today to receive for him the honor of a distinguished award. The third, Doctor Elihu Thomson, who came to this country from England, long ago blazoned his name upon the industry."

Could Weston have chosen better company? There was something so essentially right about the scientific approach of these men— quiet, self-effacing, abhorrent of self-advertising—that each helped to define and to raise the stature of the others.

The fourth and last of his honors came to Edward Weston as a very old man. This was the Benjamin Lamme medal of the American Institute of Electrical Engineers in 1932, and again an award which he was unable to journey the many miles to accept in person. At the time he received it, he was one of only six living charter members of the Institute.

10

In 1924, at the age of seventy-four years, Weston relinquished active direction of the Instrument Company, to become Chairman of the Board of Directors. His great work in electrical measurements was largely done, for he had established the world's foremost instrument-making company and had piloted it through thirty-six years of infancy into vigorous youth. He had fought its every battle himself and had seen it through every crisis in the laboratory, on the manufacturing floor, and in the courtroom. Probably there has

never been a company in the history of the United States so completely fathered and nurtured by one man. No other electrical
pioneer, certainly, kept anything like the control that Weston did,
of the products and ramifications of his inventive genius. While
Thomson, Sprague, Westinghouse, Edison himself, faded into the
background as the industries they had created grew to full strength,
Weston never for a moment lost his place at the head of electrical-
instrument making. If he had chosen to do so he could have remained the driving force of his industry till he died, and no one
would have advised him to quit.

But after fifty-four years of constant expenditure of energy he
was tired. At last he wanted to sit on the sidelines and look on;
cheer the team when he felt like it, coach them occasionally, and
simply keep the score.

His health had caved in the year before, when his wife had died.
Though she had never shared his hard work or his triumphs, he
missed her badly. He wanted to withdraw now, take account of stock,
and plan for a peaceful old age. His son Edward had come along
most gratifyingly, developing a decided talent for management. He
was content now to let him run the business.

Weston had a little old safe which he turned over to the engineering department when he retired. In the process of clearing it out,
Goodwin found one of the drawers locked. Inside, when he opened
it, was a quantity of radium. Weston had meant to experiment with
it some day but in the press of more practical matters had put it away
and forgotten it.

Another tribute to the ambitious mind which meant to play a part
in every branch of science, and failed to do so only because the days
and nights were not long enough!

II

All his life Weston had remained a subject of His Majesty the
English King. Now, preparing to retire, he decided to become an
American. Papers were taken out for him and on the thirteenth of
November, 1923, he became a citizen of the United States. Nobody
in the world but himself would have known the difference if he had
remained English till his death. He had become a citizen of the

world, and a valuable one, regardless of his flag. It may be that Weston had more than a general motive in taking out his citizenship papers. He may suddenly have become interested in politics and decided that he must make his weight felt at the polls. We shall never know.

Retirement, to Edward Weston, at the age of seventy-four, did not mean idleness. For the first few years he wandered restlessly about, missing his wife, missing his regular going to work, missing the inexhaustible redundance of the lawsuits. He had accumulated a splendid library, and this, in the hands of a paid librarian, afforded him real pleasure. The publishers all knew of Weston's passion for books and regularly sent him new volumes on approval. Many of them he kept, especially those that had to do with the strange interregnum between wars, into which he and the rest of the world were blindly plunging.

Shortly after he was eighty years old, the inventor bought a large mansion in Montclair, N. J., formerly occupied by the Van Vleck family. He had not followed the modern world into a compact, efficient little house. He was still the erect, quick-stepping Englishman whose taste in homes had always been a trifle baronial. He wanted his last years to be spent in a place big enough to "turn around in." Here he came to live with a housekeeper and a resident nurse to look after him, his daily routine enlivened by the frequent runnings in and out of his three charming little granddaughters. Walter had died in 1926, increasing the gloom of his father's loneliness by accentuating the fact that he had never really known or approved of his elder son. Such are the dark threads in the fabric of old age.

When he moved into the great Montclair house the old man called in a bevy of electricians and carpenters. "Now," he said, with something of his former spirit, "I want the best electrified place in town. Don't ask me what I want, except to consult me as to the lighting for the pictures. But omit nothing, mind." He was thinking, perhaps, of the old home on High Street, where he had installed the first private electric light plant in Newark—a dynamo with a gas engine to drive it, and storage batteries of his own design.

He took his nurse, piled into his car, and had himself driven all over New York City to find hangings, rugs, new furniture. He felt remarkably happy and able again.

It was a source of broad satisfaction to him that in 1924 the Weston Electrical Instrument Company had been incorporated, symbolically moving into a new and secure mansion of its own. Until that moment it had been his own personal property, a monument to a lifetime of travail, but lately an increasing burden as if, indeed, it were a monument and he the pedestal which alone held its weight aloft. Incorporation at last placed it beyond the fortunes and talents of any one individual; in a sense bequeathed it to posterity for all the world to enjoy.

It was now that Weston called in his lawyers and wrote his will, as accurate in detail and as pungently conceived in its bequests as though he were again sitting up all night studying court testimony and formulating a shattering reply. Typical of his good thinking was his bequest of all his laboratory apparatus and equipment to the Newark College of Engineering, together with his general technical library of many thousands of volumes, and sufficient funds to house and maintain it. Beyond this he entrusted to them his drawings and the designs for his many patents and discoveries, as well as a wealth of papers and other data concerned with the lively history of electrical engineering.

Sadly, if with deep gratitude, President Allan R. Cullimore of the College wrote, after Edward Weston had died:

"This material will be gathered together and arranged in a manner which will form a proper record of his contribution to science and technology. This will take a long time, but if it be done properly and with enlightenment and a sympathetic appreciation of the part Dr. Weston played in the general advance of science, it will constitute an exhibit whose influence will extend far beyond the walls of our institution or the limits of this particular community."

It is as a small part of this general project that this book has been written. If Weston were alive today, he would probably find much fault with this short and too cursory biography. Who knows but its author would be hailed into court even, with a bevy of attorneys after him! But at any rate, the work has been done with affection

and respect and with an honest attempt to set down the man in his
true greatness.

### 12

While he was scouring the metropolis for house furnishings, Weston's eye fell upon a luxurious motor cruiser in a display window.
It occurred to him suddenly that he had not owned a yacht for some
time. Why not go back to sea again? Very shortly, he was set up
with a fine little vessel—captain, crew, and all—and entered into
the last phase of his life. Now, for the first time in eighty years, he
was having fun for fun's own sake.

So, in whites and a captain's cap, Weston sat in the beautifully
appointed cockpit of his private vessel and wished that he could still
go into court. . . .

Instead, he cruised, and as he cruised, something of the old vigor
for work came back to him. He proposed to scour the eastern sea-
board, and to leave no bay or inlet or harbor unlearned. The old
fervor—to face the problem, whether it be arc lamps or incandescents, dynamo losses or regulators, the delicate movements of measuring instruments, or the third-place decimal of voltage in a standard
cell; whether it be golf, billiards, fishing; the shooting of clay
pigeons or the commanding of a yacht—it must be done well, done
thoroughly, done with integrity, done with an accuracy and attention to detail that counted no cost. . . .

### 13

On August 21, 1936, *The New York Times* said:

Dr. Edward Weston, scientist, is dead. Dr. Weston died fifteen minutes
after arriving home in a private ambulance from New London, Conn. He
was stricken aboard his yacht, the Lorna Doone III, at New Bedford, after
having attended the yacht races off Newport, R. I., and traveled on his yacht
to New London. The cause of his death was cerebral hemorrhage.

He died, as he would have wished, with his boots on, in the midst
of a voyage of discovery.

# Index